THE FRI

Jake Lorrimer was Stephanie's boss, and best friend—and the only person to know her secret. What was going to happen now that he was trying to change the nature of their relationship?

Books you will enjoy
by PENNY JORDAN

DARKER SIDE OF DESIRE

Saving the life of Sheikh Ahmed's young orphaned nephew had been a frightening experience for Claire Miles, and then the Sheikh had proposed that she should go out to the Middle East and look after the boy. But there was one condition—to safeguard Saud's life she would have to masquerade as his mother, with the arrogant and contemptuous Raoul D'Albro as the father!

RULES OF THE GAME

All her life Vanessa had accepted the fact that she was second rate compared to her stunning cousin Nadia; and she had harboured no resentment at being pushed into the background while Nadia's success as a model flourished. But that was until Jay Courtland mistook *her* for Nadia . . .

CAMPAIGN FOR LOVING

Why had Blake Templeton decided to re-enter Jaime's life? Could it have anything to do with the attacks on her about the sale of the Abbey? But surely he would not endanger the life of his wife and daughter? Would he?

WHAT YOU MADE ME

A week ago Philippa's life had been relatively uncomplicated. But that was before Scott Garson had strode back into it, wanting revenge for what he thought she had done to him eleven years ago. . .

THE FRIENDSHIP BARRIER

BY

PENNY JORDAN

MILLS & BOON LIMITED
15–16 BROOK'S MEWS
LONDON W1A 1DR

First published in Great Britain 1984 by Mills & Boon Limited

© Penny Jordan 1984

Australian copyright 1984 Philippine copyright 1985 This edition 1985

ISBN 0 263 74949 5

Set in Monophoto Plantin 11 on 12 pt. 01–0285 – 47771

Made and printed in Great Britain by Richard Clay (The Chaucer Press) Ltd, Bungay, Suffolk

CHAPTER ONE

'STEPH, you're late. It's gone seven. You're normally back by six. What happened?' Annette asked roguishly. 'Did that gorgeous boss of yours want you to work late?'

'Can't stop to chat now,' Stephanie apologised to her flatmate as she hurried through the small sitting room. 'Jake's picking me up in half an hour.'

'Jake?' Annette's eyebrows lifted. 'Do you call him that at work? Catch me daring to call my boss anything other than Mr James.'

Stephanie was too used to Annette's curiosity about her relationship with Jake to make any comment. Initially, when she arrived in London, she had lived alone, but after . . . but Jake had suggested when she started appearing heavy-eyed and exhausted in the office after her nightmare broken nights that she get a flatmate.

Annette was pleasant enough in her way; a secretary like herself, working for the chairman of a large insurance company. She had a fiancé who was in the army and whom she saw at irregular intervals. Yes, Annette would have been the ideal flatmate if it wasn't for her constant curiosity about Jake.

'Where's he taking you tonight, then?'

Sighing, as she stripped off her neat office suit and blouse, Stephanie responded through her half-closed bedroom door, 'The première of the new Blaize Dartford film.'

'Wow! That should be really something. The love scenes are supposed to be . . .'

Almost automatically, Stephanie shut her ears against the end of Annette's comment, dismayed but not surprised to see that her hands were shaking as she finished undressing.

In their small bathroom she showered quickly, automatically avoiding any confrontation with her own naked reflection. Back in her room, she opened her wardrobe and selected the cocktail suit she planned to wear for the evening. The matt black fabric with the velvet detailed embroidery on it was the perfect foil for her pale skin. Her hair cascaded past her shoulders in deep rich chestnut waves. For work she always wore it in a neat coil. Her wardrobe held few clothes but what there was was good. Working as Jake's secretary-cum-personal assistant, she felt she owed it to him to dress the part. As the senior partner in a very prestigious London firm of estate agents, he came in daily contact with the wealthy, and, as Stephanie had soon learned, looks and appearance *did* count. During the two years she had worked for him she had cultivated an air of cool remoteness which put off those male clients who were, initially, too familiar. She was well aware of the nickname they had given her in the outer office. The 'Ice Maiden' they called her, but she didn't care. They were not to know that she had deliberately chosen to encase herself in an unthawable protective shell. Only Jake knew that, and why. Jake . . . She glanced at her watch. Twenty-past seven, and Jake was always on time.

Her suit looked dressy, and yet formal, her long slim legs encased in pale tights, the delicacy of her ankle bones enhanced by the slender-heeled shoes she was wearing.

Deftly applying her make-up, she stood back critically to study her handiwork. Her eyes were a deep rich hazel that sometimes turned emerald, her face a delicate oval with high cheek bones and a small straight nose.

It was too late to do anything with her hair other than let it curl loosely on to her shoulders. Perfume was something Stephanie never wore, just as she never applied more than a bare trace of soft, pink lipstick to the ripely full curves of her mouth.

'Umm. I wish I was tall and leggy,' Annette complained when Stephanie emerged into their sitting room. 'What is it with you and Jake?' she enquired curiously. 'You work for him, he takes you out, you seem very close, and yet he dates other women . . . glamorous ones, too.'

'Jake is my friend and my employer,' Stephanie cut in sharply. As always, when Annette questioned her like this, she could feel the self-defensive antennae prickling warningly. It was true though. Jake *was* her friend, *and* her employer . . . and so much more that could never be said . . . she was tied to him with bonds that no one who had not shared her experience could understand. Jake knew more about her than another living soul. He had been there when . . . He had been the one who had helped her to build up her life again. He knew and understood . . .

'And not your lover ...?' the disbelieving comment penetrated Stephanie's thoughts.

'No ... not my lover.' She made the denial instinctively, her whole body registering a cold shudder she couldn't hide.

Annette frowned. 'Steph, what's the matter? You obviously like him, you *must* do, and he's one hell of an attractive man. You wouldn't see *me* turning him down, and yet when I suggest there might be something physical about your relationship, you look as sick as though I'd suggested something obscene.'

The abrupt buzz of the door bell saved her from the need to respond. Even though she knew it would be Jake, Stephanie kept the chain hooked on the door as she eased it open until she could see his tall, dinner-suited figure.

'Ready?'

As she opened the door, Jake stepped to one side to let her precede him. He was the only man of her acquaintance who understood her need to keep a physical distance between them, but then of course Jake knew the reason why. Was it really only two years since they had first met?

She had gone to his office to be interviewed for the position of his secretary and they had hit it off straight away. She had been quite new to London then. An orphan who had been brought up by elderly grandparents, she had been on her own since she was seventeen, and, because of that, at twenty-one she had developed a poise and self-confidence that made her seem older.

Jake had been thirty then, a tall, dark man, who was pleasant on the surface but to whom she suspected there were uncharted and potentially dangerous depths, a man who always kept something of himself back, and she had liked that reticence, just as she had liked the way his cool, grey eyes had acknowledged her physical attractiveness and then dismissed it as he interviewed and assessed her on her qualifications and mental qualities alone.

They had worked well together that first month, each allowing the other to preserve a certain distance. Stephanie had learned quite early in life that she was attractive to the male sex, and she had also learned the price she was supposed to pay for being attractive. She had lost count of the number of men who had propositioned her and been in turn angry and contemptuous when she had turned them down. They seemed to expect, because she was a reasonably pretty girl, that she would gladly pay for their compliments and admiration by sharing their beds. Perhaps, because of the slightly old-fashioned atmosphere in which she had been brought up, Stephanie had a different set of values. Marriage, or even finding the right man wasn't particularly to the forefront of her mind. She had a good job which she enjoyed and Jake had told her that it would involve a certain amount of foreign travel, especially to Florida where his firm was involved in certain time-sharing holiday schemes, and she was quite happy where she was. Although she got on well enough with the other girls in the office, she didn't have any intimate female friends. Her position as Jake's secretary and PA meant that she was much higher up in the office hierarchy than the other secretaries, who tended to treat her rather cautiously. This she didn't mind. She had learned to cope with loneliness as a child, and had grown to almost prefer a certain amount of solitude. For instance, then she would never have dreamed of sharing her flat with anyone . . . but all that had changed, and now there were nights when she woke up in fevered sweats, longing to scream out but knowing she could not. Nights when the knowledge that Annette was only on the other side of a thin partition wall was the only thing that kept her sane.

Sane . . . As Jake opened the passenger door of his XJ6, she repressed a bitter grimace. At first, she had pleaded with Jake to set her free from their contract. She couldn't work for him any more, she had told him, but he had refused. He had endured her tears and her depressions . . . almost her hatred at times, and they had both emerged with a different view of one another. Their friendship was perhaps the most important single thing in her life, Stephanie admitted. She loved her job, but she could always find another one, she could never find another friend like Jake.

And yet there were areas of Jake's life that were closed to her. Closed to her because that was the way she wanted it. She knew he had other women friends . . . women who, unlike her, *did* share his bed. Jake had never made any secret of the fact that he was a fully functioning sexual being —unlike her.

She knew that he had once been engaged. He had told her that during one of her bad times, sharing with her the grief he had felt when his fiancée had been killed in a car accident. He had been very young at the time, barely twenty-three, and, as far as she knew, he now had no plans to marry. Why should he? He owned a lovely old Manor House in the Cotswolds; a superb London flat; and was a frequent visitor at the best hotels in Florida. He enjoyed the freedom of his bachelor life. But, if he did marry . . . She shuddered, not wanting to think about such a possibility.

'Something wrong?'

As always, he was acutely perceptive to her mood. At work they never touched on personal subjects, but now they weren't at the office.

'Nothing.'

'Umm . . . Not very communicative tonight, are you?' He sounded more amused than annoyed, and, as always, Stephanie was aware of how much self-control he had. As she stared out of the car window the disturbing thought came to her that Jake would never allow anyone to see something of himself that he did not want them to, and that included her. She knew from the office gossip and from what she read in the papers that Jake dated several very beautiful women; women who were known to be choosy, not just about the wealth and looks of their lovers, but also about their sexual prowess, and yet, when he was with her, Jake projected an image so totally devoid of any sexual connotation that she found it hard to imagine that other side of him.

But it did exist . . . She shivered, not realising

that Jake had noticed until he frowned. 'Cold? I'll turn the booster on. Autumn seems to have come early this year.'

It was only September, but it had been a particularly good summer. Even Stephanie's fair skin had tanned, although, unlike the other girls in the office, her tan only extended as far as her arms and legs. The flat did possess a small private garden, but not even there had she been able to bring herself to put on even a swimsuit. She knew that her reluctance in that direction had caused raised eyebrows the last time she had gone with Jake to Florida. The wives of his business associates had hardly been able to believe that she didn't want to take advantage of their hot sun. As always, Jake had been the one to come to her rescue.

'Stephanie burns easily,' he had said casually, and the matter had been dropped. Only they knew the reason she was so reluctant to expose any more of her body in public than she needed to. Physical pain, and even terror, could fade in time, but mental shame, that was something that never died. Jake had initially suggested a psychiatrist, but she had been so vehemently opposed to his suggestion that he had let it drop. What could talking to someone else tell her that she didn't know already? That she had nothing to feel ashamed about? That she wasn't to blame? That she wasn't the only person to be sexually attacked? Quite unconsciously, she gave a small moan. Jake braked, and, despite the darkness of the car, Stephanie was conscious of him turning towards her.

'Are you all right?'

'Fine . . .' Her voice was rawly husky, and she knew he had picked up on the hesitancy in it.

'This wouldn't be a ploy to get out of this première, would it?' As always, he sounded lazily amused rather than annoyed . . . 'You know that James Tavener expects us to be there.'

James Tavener was one of their wealthiest clients. He had engaged Jake's firm to help him find a London apartment, and the American film producer had also invited Jake and herself to be his guests at tonight's première.

'Of course not. I'm quite looking forward to it.'

In the darkness of the car, she felt Jake tense, and wondered what on earth she had done to prompt such a reaction. The last time he had tensed like that had been . . . she frowned, remembering the incident. It had been when she had been reaching into a tall filing cabinet and had almost lost her balance. Jake had reached out to steady her, and she had gripped his arm instinctively, until, quite suddenly, the warm male smell of him and the physical reality of his masculinity had overwhelmed her in drowning waves of panic, and she had recoiled from him, shiveringly. But that had been six months ago, and Jake had been careful not to touch her since. She hadn't needed to explain to him as she might have done to someone else. Jake knew exactly how she felt and why . . .

'Have you read the advance press releases?'

'No.'

'Umm . . .'

They had to park some little distance away

from the cinema. Jake, courteous as always, walked alongside her on the outer edge of the pavement. London was quite busy, and there were other première-goers heading in the same direction as them. A gang of youths walking towards them accidentally jostled Stephanie on the crowded pavement. A sensation not unlike that she had experienced when first learning to swim overtook her. She felt as though she were gasping for breath, fighting to stay alive, as waves of panic seized her, and then Jake's voice, even and calm, subdued the waves, and the nightmare was gone.

'All right?' His voice sounded faintly tight as he looked into her pale face.

'Fine,' she lied. 'Where are we meeting the Taveners?'

'We're to go straight up to their box. There's going to be a VIP line-up which James will be part of. Apparently, we can go in this way,' he added, indicating a small back door to the theatre.

Having shown the pass James Tavener had given him, they were shown up to a sumptuous box, with an excellent vew of the screen. Half an hour later they were joined by their hosts. The curtain went up.

'Watch this boy,' James Tavener instructed them, 'he's going places. He's going to make Gere look very much yesterday's man. We had a tussle getting some of the scenes past the censor . . . nothing smutty or vulgar in them—but . . .'

'But they make your toes curl up and your insides melt,' Livy Tavener laughed, smiling across at Stephanie. 'At least, they do mine, for all that he's at least twenty years my junior . . .'

The Taveners were laughing. Jake was smiling that cool, imperturbable smile he used whenever he didn't want anyone to know what he was feeling, and Stephanie tried to smile in response, only her mouth felt stiff, refusing to respond to the commands of her brain. Fortunately, the lights had gone down, so no one else could see her expression, but Jake . . . As she forced herself to concentrate on the screen, Stephanie wondered if he had known the content of the film beforehand.

What on earth was the matter with her? Sex scenes were common nowadays; she could hardly switch on the television without seeing someone parading about in the nude. But she could always switch the television set off again, whereas here . . . She realised that James Tavener was talking to her and tried to concentrate.

'We had a lot of problems with the rape scene . . .' he told her. 'I mean we wanted something realistic, but only to get across the girl's anguish, so that the audience could appreciate what comes later with Blaize. You see, this girl avoids all contact with men, and then she meets this guy, and . . .'

'Let her watch it for herself, James,' Livy Tavener interrupted. 'Honestly, this film's his baby, and he's crazy about it,' she told Stephanie. 'He's hoping it will get an "Oscar". It certainly deserves one. Laura Howard and Blaize play their parts so realistically. The emotion between them almost reaches out to enfold you . . .'

Stephanie tried to stand up. She had to get away. She couldn't sit here and watch this film. Panic dashed over her in waves, her body alternately hot and then cold. Dimly, she was aware of Jake's fingers curling round her wrist, lean and firm, imparting a steadying warmth to her frozen skin.

'Sit down . . .' The quiet command helped to steady her.

'Jake, I can't watch this . . .' she pleaded huskily, 'You know . . .'

'Yes, I know,' he broke in softly, 'but you can't keep on running for ever, Steph. Some time, you're going to have to stop and turn round and confront your fears. Tonight might be as good a time as any.'

'You brought me here deliberately,' she whispered agonisedly. 'You knew . . .'

'Yes, I knew,' he agreed emotionlessly. 'Now sit down again unless you want the Taveners to get curious. I'm sure James would be thrilled to discover that he's got the best critic of Laura Howard's performance he could ever have sitting right next to him.'

Stephanie drew in a sharply painful breath at the cruelty of his comment. Never once before had Jake exhibited anything other than patience and consideration. Not since that night when he had taken her home to his flat, when he had washed her lacerated skin and talked to her in that soft comforting voice that had calmed her panic and fears, coaxing her to give him all the details of her attack, had he talked about what had happened to her. Oh, he had tried on several occasions, less frequently now, because on each occasion she had shied away from the subject, reacting with such emotional pain and distress that he had let it drop.

'Jake, please, I can't sit here and watch this . . .' she pleaded in anguish. 'Please . .'

'Stephanie, it's been close on two years,' he said quietly, 'and it's not getting any better If anything, it's getting worse.'

'No!'

'No? Then tell me how many men you've dated in the last two years, and how many of them have you allowed to kiss or touch you? I can tell you how many,' he said quietly when she sat frozen, unable to respond, 'None. Don't you think I know, Steph? I've only got to watch the way you recoil from me if I so much as brush against you accidentally. I practically have to chart a course across my office so that I keep out of your prescribed boundaries. Look, I know what happened to you . . .'

'Nothing happened to me,' she bit out the words sharply. On her lap her hands were folded into small fists, her nails biting into her palms. That Jake of all people should turn on her like this, and so unexpectedly. She couldn't believe it. She couldn't endure the pain ripping through her, pain like none she had ever known.

'You were almost raped,' Jake reminded her, 'violated in the most brutal and unforgivable way by a gang of youths who had deliberately lain in wait for you, and attacked you and you would have been raped if I hadn't happened to hear you scream.' He broke off when she covered her ears, her voice strained and almost unrecognisable as her tortured throat managed to admit a husky, 'No . . . no, you promised we would never have to talk about it . . . Jake . . .'

'Hey you two, aren't you interested in the film?' James Tavener's voice interrupted them, and Stephanie sank back into her seat, refusing to turn her face in Jake's direction, her whole body trembling with reaction. Even now, she couldn't believe what had happened. That Jake . . . She tried to keep her attention on the screen, but in her emotional state that was even worse. With morbid fascination, she watched Laura Howard enact what was almost a replay of what had happened to her, only *her* attackers had been a group of youths who caught the same bus home as her at night. Most evenings, they made comments as they waited for the bus, called out remarks, and generally tormented Stephanie with their presence, which was always faintly sexually threatening. And then, one night, she had worked late, and when she had emerged into the alleyway at the back of the office, they had been waiting for her. It had been December, and bitterly cold. She had been wearing boots and a thick coat which, she thought later, had helped to save her. How they had found out where she worked, she had never discovered, although Jake suspected that they must have followed her.

She had barely had time to do anything more than scream once before they attacked her. Even now, she had nightmares about those moments before Jake had arrived, alerted by her single scream. If he hadn't been on the way downstairs ... if she hadn't screamed right at that moment ... Their hands had seemed to be everywhere, tearing at her clothes, their obscene words and laughter almost as bad as their physical violation.

Jake's unexpected appearance had given him an advantage over them, and he had soon dispersed them, but not before Stephanie had been almost stunned by a vicious slap across her face, her blouse and bra ripped in huge rents which revealed her breasts, long vicious weals along her arm where she had fought to prevent them pulling off her coat. But the worst of it had been her own memories vividly replayed over and over again as Jake bundled her into his car and drove her to his apartment. She had been almost incoherent with shock and fright, retreating like a terrified animal when he tried to come near her. In the end she had fainted through sheer terror, unable to recognise friend from foe, only knowing that the hands that touched her were male and that the scent reaching her nostrils was masculine and therefore to be feared.

When she came round, she was in Jake's bathroom. She had never been in his apartment before and was in no condition to appreciate the masculine decor of marble and gold, and she had shuddered convulsively away from the touch of Jake's fingers, only to discover that he had removed her torn clothes and she was wearing only her bra and panties.

'Stephanie, you're quite safe. I just want to clean those cuts. Then I'm going to give you a glass of brandy, and put you to bed in my spare

bedroom. If you like, I'll call a doctor for you . . .
and tomorrow we can call the police.'

'No . . . No police,' she had made the plea in
abject terror. There had been so much adverse
publicity about the police's handling of rape cases
that she felt she couldn't endure the humiliation
she had read of other women's suffering.

'Stephanie . . .'

'No . . . please . . .'

In the end, he had given way, and she had
remained in his flat not for one night but for
three, terrified by every single alien sound, her
nervous system totally destroyed. Jake stayed
with her, and on the third day he had made her
talk; had made her re-live the trauma of her
attack. She had cried and protested, hating him
for what he was doing to her, and he had held her
in his arms, soothing her, stroking her like a child
. . . Stephanie frowned. This was the first time
she had allowed herself to think back to the time
of her attack, and she had forgotten that Jake had
held her and touched her, and that she had
welcomed his touch. Because it had been
paternal, she told herself, because she had been
so distraught that she had needed the comfort of
physical contact more than she feared it.

Gradually she had recovered, or at least
outwardly she had seemed to do so. Only she and
Jake knew that, inwardly . . . inwardly she would
never recover. When she dreamed, it was of hard
male hands tearing at her clothes, her screams of
panic suppressed until she felt she was suffocating
on them. Only with Jake did she feel safe and that
was because she knew he had no sexual interest in

her whatsoever. Jake knew and understood about what had happened to her, but not even Jake knew about the guilt buried deep inside her soul; the hateful, destructive feeling that whispered treacherously that somehow she had been to blame; that somehow she had given them the impression that . . . that what? That she had wanted to be raped? She shuddered sickly. Ever since she had taken care that no one could ever accuse her of encouraging any man, however tenuously.

She knew that Annette was curious about her relationship with Jake, who she admitted she found sexually attractive. Stephanie also knew that Annette did not believe her when she said their relationship was strictly platonic, but she was immune to any sensation of physical attraction now. The thought of any man touching her made her feel acutely ill.

'Now . . . just watch this scene . . .'

Stephanie came to at the sound of James Tavener's voice to realise the film had progressed considerably. Her body froze as she realised that this was the 'sex scene' James had been discussing earlier. She didn't want to watch, but her eyes seemed to be riveted to the screen against her will. Blaize Dartford was as dark as Jake and a similar age, his eyes blue where Jake's were grey. Even his voice seemed to have the same husky timbre, and it seemed to Stephanie in her highly charged emotional state that it was Jake up there on the screen, that it was his hands, and mouth, his body that made slow and deliberately sensuous love to the girl on the bed

with him. Stephanie wanted to deny the illusion,
but it wouldn't be denied, and her body burned
hot and cold as she tried to shut out the images
on the screen. Laura Howard had researched her
part well, and no one watching could not be
convinced of her anguish and uncertainty,
although, unlike her, Laura wanted to make love,
Stephanie thought. Laura wanted to overcome
her fears, whereas she was revolted and terrified
about the thought of physical intimacy with
anyone. At last, she managed to close her eyes
and blot out the final few moments of the film.

The Taveners insisted on them joining them
for supper and, while they waited for their meal
to be served, James turned to Jake and asked with
a grin, 'I'll bet there wasn't a woman in the
cinema tonight who wasn't mentally imagining
herself in Laura's place . . .'

'Well, Stephanie,' Jake challenged, 'Do you
agree with that statement?'

What could she say? To agree meant agreeing
that she had wanted to be Laura; that she had
wanted to be made love to . . . not by Blaize, but
by Jake, because it was his face she had seen on
the screen, his hands she had witnessed caressing
the soft, female flesh of his partner . . .

'Stephanie's probably one of the few women at
the première tonight who wasn't bowled over by
Blaize,' Livy Tavener interrupted with a grin in
Stephanie's direction. 'If anything, Jake's even
more attractive.'

'Why, I thank you, ma'am . . .' Jake drawled,
not in the least embarrassed.

'Jake and I are friends . . . nothing more,'

Stephanie put in hurriedly, her face scarlet with embarrassment as she read the speculation in James Tavener's eyes. 'Isn't that so, Jake . . .?'

'I never contradict a lady,' Jake drawled. He was watching her with hard grey eyes, and it came to Stephanie with a shock that he had never looked at her like that before—almost as though he actively disliked her. A gulf seemed to yawn open at her feet, ground which she had thought of as safe and familiar suddenly very treacherous. What had happened between them? Why had Jake chosen tonight to bring up the past? Intuitively she knew it was not simply because of the similarity between her own attack and the film, and then she remembered Jake asking her if she had read the advance press releases. He must have known she had not because, if she had, she would never have agreed to attend, and yet he obviously had known what to expect and he had not warned her. What was she to read into that? Was he tired of their friendship? Tired of her emotional dependence on him, her need to use him as a barrier behind which she hid from all other men? Suddenly, she was desperately afraid; afraid of being alone . . . of losing Jake's friendship, and most of all of the cold condemnation she had read in his eyes.

CHAPTER TWO

SUPPER seemed to drag on, with Stephanie feeling increasingly miserable. The Taveners were both in good spirits, and James Tavener beamed at her, telling her that he always enjoyed having supper at the Ritz. 'Kind-a finishes the evening off properly,' he told her, as he ordered a second bottle of champagne.

'No?' he exclaimed, lifting his eyebrows when she refused a second glass. 'Jake, why don't you two go and dance?'

Jake had been engaged in conversation with Livy Tavener, but he glanced across at Stephanie with a querying lift of his eyebrows.

'No, really, I'd rather not,' she started to protest, shivering as she saw the chill contempt invade Jake's eyes. What had she done to merit that look? He knew how much she abhorred physical contact, and indeed, one of the things she most appreciated in his treatment of her was the fact that he was always so meticulously careful about avoiding touching her.

It seemed to Stephanie that it was hours before the others were ready to leave. She did not have to work in the morning and there was no reason why she should not have a late night. She wasn't sleepy, if anything, she was too keyed up and awake, but she was longing for the privacy of her flat, to the extent that she desperately wished that Annette wasn't going to be there.

At last, they were saying their goodbyes. She walked with Jake to where he had left the car in total silence. There had been silences between them before—comfortable, comforting silences when the depth of their friendship had made social chit-chat unnecessary, but this was a different silence, as deep and cold as a Siberian winter, and Stephanie quailed inwardly. What was happening between them? There had been no indication of what was to come when Jake returned from the States earlier in the week. He had been gone for ten days; this time, she had not accompanied him because she had picked up a tummy bug which had kept her off work, and he had seemed all right when she had met him at the airport. But there had been that incident when she had moved forward to help him with his hand luggage, and their fingers had brushed acci- dentally. Jake had recoiled as though he had been stung, she remembered. At the time, she had simply thought he had been withdrawing out of concern for her, but his withdrawal had been sharper than one that sprang from mere concern. He had looked ... yes, almost pale, she remembered now, his eyes unusually bleak, and he had been curt and off-hand with her in the car, but, because she had been concentrating on driving the large XJ6, she had not paid too much attention, simply thinking that he was suffering from jet lag. Gnawing her lip, Stephanie suddenly remembered the venomous comments one of his ex-girlfriends had made to her last

Christmas. Susy Waldron had been dating Jake for about six weeks at the time, and Stephanie had never expected the confrontation that came late one afternoon when Jake had cancelled a date with Susy because he had to go out of town on business.

She had arrived in the office, slightly tipsy, demanding to see him, and when Stephanie calmly explained that he wasn't available, Susy had refused to leave. 'I know all about you, you know,' she had commented tipsily, making Stephanie almost faint with shock, 'all about your "friendship" with Jake . . . but it won't last for ever,' she hissed viciously, 'Jake isn't the sort of man who could ever be content with a platonic relationship with a woman—even a woman as dull as you. For some reason you now interest him—but one day he'll grow bored with you. Like I just said, Jake is a very sexy man, even if you don't have enough feminine hormones in your body to recognise it.'

Eventually, Stephanie had persuaded her to leave. At the time, she hadn't paid much attention to her comments. How could a woman like her understand the very special relationship she had with Jake? She had been almost contemptuous of the other woman, she realised now . . . just as she had tended to be slightly contemptuous of all Jake's womanfriends; glamorous, greedy predators, without a single thought in their heads that did not concern the appeasement of their appetites, but what she had never done before was question why Jake always chose women of that type. From the little he had told her about his dead fiancée, Stephanie had gained the impression that she had been both attractive and intelligent, but, like her, Jake had been hurt too much to commit himself to any permanent relationship since. He had lost the woman he loved; she had lost her trust in his sex and her ability to respond to it sexually, and she had thought that their friendship had been built on rock so steady that nothing could ever shake its foundations. Had she been wrong? In the darkness of the car, she darted a glance at his impassive profile, noticing, with something approaching shock, the deeply bitter lines grooving alongside his mouth. How long had those been there? And that cold withdrawal she sensed increasingly tonight, when had that been born? Icy fingers of alarm touched her spine. Had Jake perhaps at last found someone who could be both lover and friend . . .? Was that why . . .? What if he had, she asked herself, appalled by the intensity of feeling her own thoughts stirred up. Surely she wasn't so criminally possessive and insecure that she didn't want Jake to find happiness with another woman? She was his friend, for Heaven's sake, and, as his friend . . . as his friend . . . She dragged her thoughts away from the tortuous paths they were treading as she realised that they were not heading for her flat but for Jake's apartment.

'Not more work tonight, surely?' she mock groaned. It wasn't unknown for Jake to ask her to work late, or even to telephone her at home during the weekend to ask her to come over to help him out with something he was working on.

These impromptu work sessions normally ended with a comfortable meal *à deux* in his apartment and a quiet evening spent together listening to his record collection. She treasured them as tranquilly enjoyable oases of peace and pleasure in the anguished pain that she sometimes felt her life had become.

Jake didn't answer, and Stephanie felt her earlier anxiety return as he turned his car into the underground car park to his block of flats. A highly efficient lift, activated by Jake's personal key, bore them upwards to his apartment.

Whenever she visited it, Stephanie was always reminded of her first visit, of coming round to find herself in Jake's bathroom, his hands clinically sexless as they removed her clothes and dealt with her lacerated arms.

A pleasant foyer gave way to the generously proportioned living room with its comfortably upholstered furniture and rich Persian rugs. Stephanie loved the ambience of Jake's apartment. Despite the fact that he lived here alone, apart from the visits of his daily cleaner, it had a 'lived in' quality of which she was always acutely conscious.

'Drink?'

When she shook her head, she saw Jake walk across to the cocktail cabinet set into the bank of rosewood cabinets, and she was surprised to see him pour a large measure of spirits for himself. He rarely drank, and tonight there had been wine with their supper, plus champagne, as well as liqueurs after the meal.

'There's no need to look at me like that,' he told her curtly, 'I'm not about to rape you.'

As always, she flinched away from the word, immeasurably hurt and shocked that he should use it when he knew how much it distressed her.

'Why wouldn't you dance with me?' he demanded abruptly, walking towards her, almost spilling his drink as he put his glass down forcefully on a gleaming table. 'Why, Stephanie' Just what is it you think my touch will do to you, contaminate you?'

Contaminate her? Inwardly, she shivered. If anyone was doing any contaminating it would surely be her . . . she was the one whose body had been violated; she was the one who would never be able to cleanse her mind of the scars it bore.

'Two damned years, and you're as terrified of being touched now as you were that night when I brought you back here.'

'That's not true,' somehow she managed to force out the hurt denial, turning away so that he wouldn't see the betraying shimmer of tears in her eyes.

'Isn't it?' His fingers tightening round her wrist wrenched her round to face him. Why had she never noticed before how intensely masculine he was . . . how dangerously sexual as he towered over her, his eyes a hard, cold grey.

'Oh, you may not scream with terror whenever I come near you, but inwardly you're still screaming, Stephanie. Inwardly, I hear you screaming whenever I get that little bit too close.'

'No . . . no. You're wrong.' He wasn't, but somehow she felt impelled to deny his accusations.

'Am I?'

His other hand caught her free wrist, holding it behind her back as he used his superior strength to propel her towards him. Centimetres from his body, Stephanie tensed her muscles, inwardly shrinking back, but the hard pressure of his arm against her waist and lower back forced her forward, until there was only the minutest gap between them.

She wanted to beg him to release her, to scream and cry for freedom, but something stronger than these instincts forced her to remain still.

'Oh, you're putting up a very good impression of not loathing touching me, but we both know the truth, don't we?'

Stephanie had to lift her head to look at him. His eyes were as cold as slate, his mouth twisting in a bitter grimace she had never seen before.

'Jake . . . please, why are you doing this?' she whispered from a painfully constricted throat. 'What have I done . . .?'

'Nothing, Stephanie,' he said sardonically, 'nothing at all. That's just it,' he added under his breath, 'you haven't done a damn thing to try to rejoin the human race. What would I need to threaten to get you to touch me of your own free will, I wonder?' he asked bitterly.

He saw the response in her eyes without her needing to voice it. 'Two years we've known one another . . . two years, when I haven't so much as laid a finger on you, and yet, even now, you shrink from me, as though I were some damned rapist.'

'Jake, please . . .'

'Jake, please . . .' he mimicked savagely back. 'Please what? Please don't touch me? Please don't let your body come anywhere near mine?'

'Jake, why are you like this?'

'Why don't you ask yourself instead why you are the way you are?' he said softly. 'Why, you recoil from me if I so much as do this.' His free hand stroked lightly down her spine, but the effect on Stephanie was electrifying. She tried to move away from the light caress, her frantic attempts to escape bringing her up against the hard leanness of Jake's body. Beneath the palm she had thrust out to push him away, she could feel the heavy beat of his heart. The sensation was so unexpected and strange that, for a moment, she simply stood there, too confused even to think.

'What's the matter, Steph?' Jake goaded. 'Surprised to find out that, unlike you, I'm not made of stone?'

'Jake, why are you being like this? I thought we were friends.'

'Friends . . .' he released her and raked angry fingers through his dark hair. 'Yes, but only on your terms, isn't that it? Tell me this, Stephanie, what kind of friendship is it that exists without trust?'

'I do trust you!'

'Do you?' He gave her a hard, enigmatic stare. 'Then prove it to me,' he said softly. 'Come over here, and kiss me.'

'I can't.'

'Then I'll just have to kiss you, won't I?' he

said calmly, coming towards her. 'Remember, Stephanie,' he said as his fingers gripped her shoulders, 'you said you trusted me.'

Stephanie made a sound deep in her throat, barely aware of the animal terror in it, as Jake slid his hands over her back, drawing her body against his. She could have broken away; some part of her was aware of that, just as it was aware that Jake wasn't using any physical pressure to bring her body close to his, but his eyes seemed to hypnotise her, draining her of the will to resist. She stood within the circle of his arms like a plastic doll, rigid and tense with the enormity of what was happening. Never once, in the two years since her attack, had Jake behaved like this, and part of her couldn't believe what he was doing now. The glitter in his eyes was that of a man starved too long of something he hungered desperately for—dimly she recognised that fact and then repudiated it, Jake was no sex-starved adolescent. So why was he doing this to her?

His hand spread out against her spine, anchoring her against his lean frame, making it impossible for her to recoil from the intimate contact he was forcing upon her. She could smell the sharp tangy scent of his aftershave, her flesh acutely conscious of the warmth of his beneath the formality of his evening clothes. Without wanting to, she became aware of him in a way she never had before, her heart thudding in a mixture of apprehension and shock. His free hand slid up her spine to tangle in the chestnut thickness of her hair. Her eyes, shocked and hurt, widened as Jake forced her to meet his.

'Your eyes are the colour of emeralds,' he murmured, 'they always go green when you're emotionally aroused.'

Stephanie jerked against the constraining pressure of his hand in her hair in objection to his choice of words, and then closed her eyes, tensing her whole body, willing him to kiss her if that was what he intended, and end her torment. Unwittingly, she had tensed her hands into small fists, and dark colour surged up under her pale skin as Jake whispered sardonically against her ear, 'You're supposed to reciprocate, not clench your fingers in anticipation of some dreadful ordeal. Relax. All I'm going to do is kiss you, Stephanie . . .'

'I can't.'

The husky admission was torn from her aching throat. She badly wanted to cry, not so much from terror now, but from shock and hurt. Why was Jake, the only person she had thought understood and appreciated how she felt, behaving like this? She could hardly equate the cold, mocking stranger he had turned into with the man she had called her friend.

'Then I'll just have to help you, won't I?' His dark head bent towards her and Stephanie closed her eyes, tensing herself to receive his kiss, her lips dry and stiff . . . She could feel the heat of Jake's hand spread against the back of her skull and she jumped nervously when his thumb brushed softly against the delicate area behind her ear. Shivers of reaction spread through her body from that brief point of contact, detonating a trembling response she couldn't conceal.

'Jake, please don't do this . . .' The request was stammered and hoarse, her lips almost too stiff to form the words.

'Open your mouth, Steph, so I can kiss you properly.' That was his only response, and one that Stephanie knew nothing could make her obey. Strangely enough, her fear that being in Jake's arms would bring back all her nightmare memories of her attack was unfounded. She was frightened, almost terrified out of her wits, but her fear had more to do with the fact that she found the sudden change in Jake totally incomprehensible than any confusion of his embrace with those she had endured at the hands of her attackers, and her biggest fear of all was that, once Jake kissed her, she would lose him as her friend. Why on earth should he want to kiss her in the first place? Even before her attack, she had been rather withdrawn with men, and never in a million years could she hope to compete with the sexual experience of the women Jake normally dated.

Her lips pressed tightly together to stop them trembling she almost gasped out loud as Jake's tongue tip brushed seductively over their tense outlines. Quivers of sensation like light, electric shocks rippled through her sensitive skin. Like an arid desert, bursting into full bloom after an unexpected shower of rain, she could feel the tension retreating and her lips softening into compliance beneath the warmth of Jake's tongue as it stroked them into bemused acceptance of his unspoken commands. Without her even giving it conscious thought, her lips parted, her dark lashes fluttered upwards for a stunned, disbelieving second as she looked into the molten greyness of Jake's eyes and knew that this was actually happening; that her body was actually quivering heatedly in response to the light play of Jake's thumb against the tender flesh of her nape; that her mouth was actually moist and warm against his, allowing him to kiss her with an intimacy she couldn't remember sharing with anyone before.

All at once, it was as though all her senses came truly alive, and she was acutely aware of everything about him; from the hard tension of his body against hers, the muscle and bone so different from her own yielding softness; to the musky, male scent of him that somehow excited and yet frightened at the same time.

She must have made some small protest because, suddenly and totally unexpectedly, she was free and Jake was three feet away from her regarding her with a look of mingled contempt and anger. Fear and misery poured through her making her ache in every nerve ending. It was almost as though she had been anaesthetised against pain and feeling, and had suddenly come tinglingly and painfully to life. She wasn't sure that she liked the sensation. Her self-confidence had been totally undermined, and she was aware, not for the first time, just how emotionally dependent she was on Jake. If he turned away from her . . .

'Come on, I'd better take you home,' Jake's brusque words cut through her anguished thoughts.

'Jake . . .' she began hesitantly, but he cut

through what she was about to say, silencing her
with a curt, 'Look, let's not have an inquest right
now. If you're looking for an explanation, let's
just say it was an experiment that went wrong.'

Too numb and exhausted by the violence of
her own emotions, Stephanie stayed silent as he
drove her home. Normally, after a late night, she
stayed at the apartment with him, but tonight he
had made no such suggestion. Was he growing
tired of her as Susy had predicted he would? All
the old insecurities she had suffered after the
attack resurfaced, and she was glad to escape
Jake's silent presence when he eventually left her
at her flat door.

After a night of disturbed and uneasy rest, she
finally fell properly asleep in the early hours and
woke up heavy-eyed and headachey well after ten
o'clock.

'Well, well, that must have been some night
last night,' Annette commented when she finally
got up. 'It isn't like you to sleep in.'

'I was tired,' Stephanie lied briefly. A glance in
her mirror before she walked into the kitchen had
shown her an unfamiliarly wan face and pain-
haunted eyes.

Somehow she got through the weekend,
busying herself with unnecessary chores, and
surveying her previous winter's wardrobe. Her
job called for her to be smartly and well-dressed,
but as she looked at the sensible suits and
severely cut blouses she had bought the previous
winter, she knew a vague but definite dissatisfac-
tion. Annette, who had nothing on for the
weekend, came into her room to watch.

'Heavens,' she exclaimed breezily, examining the growing pile of garments, 'these are almost like a uniform. If I had a figure like yours you'd never catch me wearing anything so dull. Why don't you go mad for once and get yourself something really sexy? I would if I had your figure.'

'Such as?' Stephanie enquired drily. Annette favoured flamboyant, sometimes frankly gaudy clothes that Stephanie simply could not see herself in at all. Perhaps her clothes were a little on the dull side, but at least when she was wearing them no one could accuse her of trying to attract male attention. Her appearance never presented a sexual come-on or challenge.

'Like this, for instance,' Annette pounced triumphantly, flourishing a magazine she had been reading. 'We've still got a couple of hours before the shops close. All the new season's stock should be in by now, and don't tell me you can't afford it ... with the salary I suspect Jake pays you ...'

Stephanie wasn't listening. She was staring transfixed at the photograph Annette was holding out to her. Numbly, she read the caption, 'Susy Waldron, modelling the new Galman autumn range at the home of wealthy Florida businessman, Dale Mather. Another house guest was Susy's escort, Jake Lorrimer. When asked about their romance, Susy refused to comment, but the couple were seen strolling arm in arm through Dale Mather's justifiably famous gardens almost every evening of their visit.'

'Stephanie, what's wrong with you?' Annette

demanded. 'What do you think of the dress? I can just see you in it.'

The dress in question was in soft, black angora, cut on deceptively demure lines, but Stephanie paid it scant attention. Jake and Susy together. Was that why he had kissed *her*? Because he and Susy were apart . . . because he knew that Susy did not like her. Jake was a man in whom the sensual currents ran strong and deep, and if she hadn't known it before, she knew it now. Deep enough for him to sacrifice their friendship to his desire for Susy? Had Susy perhaps demanded as the price of her love, Stephanie's own eviction from Jake's personal life?

They were questions that Stephanie could not answer. She felt as though life had suddenly cast her adrift on unfamiliar and treacherous waters with nothing to cling to for support.

More to keep her mind occupied with other thoughts than for any other reason, she allowed Annette to persuade her to go shopping. They visited the exclusive Knightsbridge store that stocked the clothes featured in the magazine and at Annette's insistence Stephanie tried on the black angora dress.

'Stunning,' was her verdict once it was on. 'It looks even better on you than it did on the model. The colour brings out the red lights in your hair,' she said critically. 'Black suits you. And what about this?' she brandished a glove-soft leather skirt in a softly muted olive-cum-khaki colour with a toning mohair jumper.

Stephanie stared at her, aghast. 'Annette, I

never wear anything like that,' she told her distastefully, 'Leather . . .'

'Leather skirts are "in" this year,' Annette argued firmly. 'Try it on, at least. This jumper is gorgeous. If we weren't saving so hard to get married, I might indulge in one myself.'

The jumper *was* lovely, Stephanie admitted when she had it on. The soft mohair caressed her skin with a sensuous warmth that made her unexpectedly aware of her own body, and, for a few seconds, she wasn't sure if she liked the sensation. Appreciation of her own sensuality wasn't something she was familiar with—that side of her nature had been suppressed, partially during her teens when she had only had her grandmother as an example, and then completely following the attack, when she had developed a morbid fear of anyone reading any hint of sexual compliance in her attitude. The satin-winged dragon motif appliqued to the front of the sweater felt unfamiliar beneath her finger tips and she had a sudden and very disturbing notion that Jake's skin would feel very much the same. Smooth, yet strong. She snatched her fingers away from the satin as though they had been stung, blushing in the privacy of her changing room at the intimacy of her thoughts. What was happening to her? She had never even thought about touching Jake before, even in the most casual of fashions, never mind imagining his nude body, and, yet, now . . . It must be the small enclosed space she was in that was making her feel so hot, she decided, quickly unfastening the studded side fastening of the leather skirt.

Perhaps it was because she was trying to come to terms with her unfamiliar feelings that she allowed Annette to persuade her into buying not only the leather skirt and the sweater, but also a matching silk shirt and the black angora dress, plus an evening suit cut to reveal the soft curves of her body, with a tiny, nipped-in waist and a low, revealing back, although when she was going to wear such a potentially provocative garment she wasn't quite sure. Even the colour—a rich sapphire blue—wasn't one she would normally have chosen.

'You'll wear it when you go out on these business dinners with Jake, of course,' Annette chastised her when she voiced her doubts as they headed for the escalator. 'Come on,' she added. 'I'm really getting into the swing of this fairy godmother thing now. I'm not letting you go back to the flat until you've bought some new underwear and you'll need new shoes . . .'

'Underwear? But . . .'

'You'll need something to wear under that suit,' Annette reminded her. 'It's practically backless, remember—unless, of course, you're planning to dispense with your bra?'

There was a wicked twinkle in her eyes as she added this last. Although slightly above medium height with a narrow waist and slender hips, Stephanie had very rounded and full breasts—a fact which she abhorred and did all she could to disguise, always wearing formal blouses and neat jackets.

'What on earth are you looking like that for?' Annette grinned. 'What I'd give to swop my 32A for your 34C! You don't know how lucky you are. Pity slinky sweaters aren't in fashion this year. I'd just love to see your Jake's face if you turned up at the office in one.' She laughed again at Stephanie's expression, and took advantage of her momentary lack of concentration to herd her into the lingerie department.

As before, Annette took charge before Stephanie could open her mouth, quickly explaining what was needed.

'How about this?' A soft pale grey silk satin camiknicker with a very low-cut back was produced for their inspection.

'Oh, it's mouthwatering, Steph, isn't it?' Annette drooled. 'And just look at this!' She held up the garment so that Stephanie could see the delicate lacy panels that comprised the top of the camiknicker. 'Go and try it on,' she urged. 'Take the suit with you to make sure the back's low enough.' The suit was produced for the saleslady's inspection, who agreed that the stock of low-backed bras they had in would not be low enough to wear under it, and, as Stephanie walked past her, Annette murmured wickedly, 'You're going to cause quite a stir the next time you go to an official dinner with your boss. I can't see much business getting done—the men will be too busy wondering whether you are or aren't and if you, are, what—it would send their temperatures rocketing if they ever found out,' she added mischievously.

The camiknickers fitted perfectly, the delicate lace cups moulding the full curves of her breasts so that her skin glowed mother of pearl through them, her nipples a deep rosy pink. The sensation of the lace and satin so close to her skin was infinitely disturbing. The garment was far too erotic for her simple tastes, Stephanie decided, but it did fit very neatly and discreetly beneath her new suit, and, in the end, she allowed Annette to badger her into buying it.

On the way home, Annette oozed self-satisfaction. 'I've been dying to get you out of all those dull correct clothes you favour for months,' she admitted cheerfully, as they prepared their evening meal, 'and those camiknickers!' She rolled her eyes and grinned. 'Personally, I've always been something of an underwear freak— nothing gaudy, or openly sexy; it's just that I adore the sensation of silks and satins next to my skin. It makes me feel good, and yet rather naughty at the same time, if you know what I mean. It's my only extravagance that Roger approves of.' She spluttered with laughter when she saw Stephanie's expression, shaking her head a little over her reserve, and Stephanie wondered a little bleakly if Susy Waldron wore silks and satins next to her skin and if Jake enjoyed touching them before he touched her.

It was alarming and extremely disturbing to find she had come so far down a road she hadn't even been aware of setting out on. Somehow her life had taken an unexpected turning, and she wasn't sure yet herself just what it was leading to; all she did know was that she feared the changes heralded, and that if she could she would have gone back to the security of a friendship with Jake which had no overtones of sexuality. How had they come to be there in the first place? It was a question she just couldn't answer.

CHAPTER THREE

WHEN Stephanie went back to work on Monday morning she admitted to a butterfly feeling of trepidation. All weekend she had kept remembering the scene at Jake's apartment—the way he had spoken to her. And the way he had kissed her, she forced herself to acknowledge.

A quick flick through her diary—an almost automatic first-thing job once she had taken off her coat—showed her that Jake had an early dental appointment. She grimaced faintly as she checked through the mail, sorting it into neat piles. Jake hated visiting the dentist, and his mood was likely to be none too good when he did arrive.

She had dealt efficiently with what she could of the post, dealt with several phone calls, including one from a would-be house seller who wanted Jake to go round to value what sounded to be an extremely promising Thames-side property, and was sitting neatly in front of her typewriter, sipping a cup of coffee, when Jake finally arrived. One side of his jaw was faintly swollen, his eyes a dark and threateningly stormy grey. He flung down his Burberry with a lack of his normal precision, his frown deepening as his glance swept over Stephanie's calm face and neatly clad body.

What was he looking for, she wondered,

hanging grimly on to the calm smile she had been practising all weekend as his scrutiny raked her, as potentially dangerous as a sharply honed razor. Even allowing for the dental visit, there was something about him this morning that sparked warning signals in her own defence system. She had been right to dread this meeting. Subtly, unbearably to her mind, and possibly irretrievably, things had changed between them.

'Messages?' Jake flung the demand at her as he walked through into his own office. Normally, his abrupt manner didn't bother her but, for some reason, this morning she found herself flushing angrily, not so much at the curtness of his voice but at the way his eyes lingered for that extra half a second on the soft swell of her breasts before he strode past her. Never once in the past had Jake ever, by so much as a glance, indicated any sexual awareness of her, but this morning . . . The buzzer on her desk distracted her and she picked up the phone.

The buzz had signalled that it was an internal call and, as she listened to one of the other partners requesting an urgent meeting with Jake, Stephanie tred to dismiss from her mind her turbulent feelings.

The urgent meeting kept him out of the office until Stephanie was about to go for lunch. He returned just as she was putting her coat on, and indicated imperiously that he wanted her to wait.

The door between their two offices was half open and, as she was waiting, Stephanie heard him pick up his own phone and punch a series of numbers into it.

Seconds later her whole body seemed to be seized in a painful paralysis as she heard him drawl, 'Susy? About tonight, I'm afraid I'm not going to be able to make it.'

Becoming aware that she was eavesdropping on his private conversation Stephanie moved disjointedly towards her own desk. Susy? Why did his relationship with Susy Waldron upset her so?

'Sorry about that,' his phone call finished, Jake walked back into her office. 'I've got to go out and see that new property this afternoon and I want you to come with me. It sounds promising. Can you manage with half an hour for lunch?'

It wasn't the first time Jake had made such a request. Normally, when they were busy, she would go out and buy them both sandwiches for lunch and they would work companionably, side by side, while they ate, but today, for some reason, she hesitated to suggest this.

'Calm, serene Stephanie,' Jake drawled, when she nodded an affirmative. 'You like the world to think nothing can penetrate through the wall, don't you? You've got "don't trespass" signs posted all round your personal space, feet high, but we both know that . . .'

Another moment, and he would be talking about Friday evening, and that was something she just couldn't endure. 'I'm on my lunch hour, Jake,' she interrupted evenly. 'Half an hour, I think you said. I'd better go . . .'

'Flight, not fight, is that it, Steph?' he jeered, as she turned away. 'What is it you're so frightened of?'

Losing your friendship, she could have said;

being alone without you, but the words were far too painful to be voiced, and, instead, she simply walked out of the office before he saw that she was trembling—Jake had very sharp eyes and extremely acute perceptions. She had known him to be brusque and even sarcastic at times before; she had never known this cutting, deliberate intention to hurt and she was at a loss to understand the reason for it.

She was back from lunch exactly on the dot. She could hear sounds of movement from Jake's office and tapped briefly on the door before going in. Jake was standing with his back to her staring out of his window. He had removed the jacket of his suit and the fine cotton shirt he was wearing clung to the taut muscles of his back. What was the matter with her, Stephanie asked herself in distraught dismay? She had seen Jake without his jacket on countless thousands of occasions in the past—she had even once arrived at his flat and found him still only half dressed, and yet she could never remember once reacting as she was reacting now. All her stomach muscles seemed to have clenched in a tight spasm and refused to unlock. Her body shook and her skin felt hot. She wanted to reach out and trace the clean line of his spine to ... He swung round, catching her off guard, and she quickly veiled her eyes, looking distractedly at the papers on his desk.

'Something wrong?'

Even without looking at him, she could sense his quick frown. It took an almost superhuman effort of will to sound casual as she murmured, 'No ... no, I'm fine. What time did you want to

leave?' Her voice was a husky, unfamiliar whisper
edged with a strain she hoped he wouldn't notice.

It was only as she followed Jake down to the
car park that she realised what was happening.
Almost for the first time in their friendship she
was lying to him, hiding her feelings from him,
and she could barely understand her own
reactions. All she could do was accept that they
were necessitated by his attitude towards her;
part of a complex and sensitive feminine defence
mechanism she had hitherto never needed to use
with Jake.

'You're quiet. Not sulking, are you?' Jake
jeered softly once they were in the car.

'Sulking?'

For a moment, she was honestly puzzled, and
then a quick flush burned her fair skin as he
drawled, 'Remember Friday night? It isn't
exactly unheard of for women to resort to sulks
when they're challenged.'

'Is that what you were doing? Challenging me?'
She forced a light laugh. 'Silly me, I thought it
was meant to be therapy. Susy's back in London
than,' she chattered on too brightly into the taut
silence that followed her previous remark. 'I saw
her photograph in *New York*.'

'Yes, she's got a modelling assignment over
here,' Jake agreed, '*Vogue*. I think we turn left
here.'

Stephanie glanced at her typewritten directions
and agreed. Perhaps it was silly of her to imagine
that things had changed between herself and
Jake, but she couldn't dismiss the fear that she
was right and that there could be no going back.

The house was every bit as enchanting as it had sounded. Surrounded by a beautifully tended and very private garden that ran down to the river and included a private mooring, it had been built in the nineteen twenties in a mock Tudor style that had mellowed attractively over the years. The owner explained, as he showed them over, that he had been promoted and was being transferred to the American parent of the company he worked for.

'My wife isn't too pleased,' he admitted wryly. 'She loves this place. We bought it shortly after we were married with a legacy I inherited.'

'It's an extremely attractive property,' Jake told him, 'and it shouldn't be too difficult to sell. One of the drawbacks might be the fact that there's only one bathroom, although, with six bedrooms and a box room, doing a conversion shouldn't be too difficult.'

The kitchen, too, was slightly old-fashioned by modern-day standards, but Stephanie loved the generous proportions of the drawing room and the comfortable family sitting room overlooking the back garden. It was with something approaching a wrench that she finally turned away from the house, glancing over her shoulder from Jake's car to catch a last glimpse of it as they drove away.

'We won't have any problem selling that,' Jake announced, as they joined the main road. 'What did you think of it?'

'I loved it,' Stephanie told him. 'It's a real family house . . .'

'Umm . . .' For some reason, her comment caused him to glance sharply at her.

'Jake . . .' she said his name uncertainly, impelled by a need that went deeper than natural reserve and self-restraint. 'Jake . . . are we still friends?' she asked huskily, not daring to look at him, 'after Friday night . . .?'

'Does our friendship mean so much to you?'

He sounded slightly amused, and Stephanie had to swallow the sharp lump of pain that had lodged in her throat.

'Yes,' she admitted honestly. 'Otherwise I wouldn't have asked you. I can't understand what's happened between us, Jake. One moment everything was as it's always been, and then, on Friday . . .'

'On Friday night, I kissed you and turned from a cherished friend to a potential enemy, is that how you see it, Steph?' He was still smiling, but this time she sensed something other than amusement underlying his words, something that eluded her and yet frightened her.

'I . . .'

'No relationship can stand still forever.'

'No . . . I can understand that you must have been missing Susy . . .' Somehow, she managed to force the words past stiff lips, praying that he wouldn't know them for the lies they were. She couldn't understand; either why he had treated her as he had, or why he had changed. He had always been so meticulous in the past about not allowing his affairs to infringe on their relationship.

'Can you? And how could you do that?' he

demanded with a quiet savagery that shocked her out of her pain, 'when, by your own admission, physical desire is something you can't experience? Or have you been lying to me, Stephanie? Can you feel it?'

'Jake, please . . . don't let's quarrel. I'm sorry if I've made you angry. Look, why don't we forget all about last Friday. Come round for dinner one evening. I'll make Pavlova for you,' she teased, mentioning his favourite dessert, only to feel her smile disappearing completely when he said with cold curtness, 'Sorry, but I won't be able to make it. I've got a pretty hectic schedule over the next few weeks.'

'Yes, of course.' The pain was so intense it was almost numbing; a silent intensity of anguish that threatened to blot out everything else. Never in a thousand nightmares had she imagined that Jake would ever refuse an olive branch from her. Even now, she was finding it hard to accept.

'Jake . . .' she reached out, nearly touching his arm, her voice unconsciously pleading.

'Stop worrying.' His words were clipped, and he didn't look at her. 'If my friendship means that much to you, Stephanie, you've got it, it's just that I think, for the time being, that we both need a little breathing space.' Watching the cynical twist to his mouth, Stephanie knew it was a statement she wasn't going to be allowed to argue about.

On the surface, nothing had changed. They still functioned perfectly together as a working team, and there were even times in the days that followed when she could have believed that their quarrel had simply been something she had imagined, if it hadn't been for the expression she occasionally surprised in Jake's eyes when she glanced up and found him watching her. It was a distant, assessing scrutiny that somehow chilled her; as though she were being weighed and found wanting.

Friday was a particularly hectic day, an apt ending for a very difficult week. When her typewriter broke down just before lunch, Stephanie had difficulty in repressing a scream of pure frustration. A telephone call to the suppliers brought a promise of help during the afternoon and the loan of another machine, and she was just replacing the receiver when the door to her office was flung dramatically open.

She had seen Susy Waldron in the flesh before, of course, but, on that occasion, she must not have registered the lintensely sexual aura the other woman projected, Stephanie reflected sickly as the model's musky perfume enveloped her. Dressed in a supple russet leather skirt and a startlingly effective top in russets and other autumnal colours, she glanced contemptuously towards Stephanie before heading for Jake's door.

'Jake . . . Jake is on the phone at the moment,' Stephanie told her shakily. 'If you'd just like to wait . . .'

'Jake won't mind my going in,' Susy said. 'He's taking me out to lunch,' she added, her pale blue eyes gleaming with unmistakable malice through the layers of expertly applied make-up she was wearing. From a distance, that careful use of cosmetics had the effect of softening and darkening her eyes, but, close to, they were unmistakably pale and very cold; so cold that Stephanie felt herself shiver and step back slightly.

'I wouldn't arrange anything for him this afternoon, if I were you,' Susy added. 'I doubt that he'll be back.'

The light on Stephanie's extension went off, indicating that Jake had concluded his call but, before she could say anything, his door opened and he stood there. As always, when he was working, he had removed his jacket. The top button of his shirt was undone, his tie slightly awry.

'Jake, darling.'

Was he really so taken in with her surface attraction that he couldn't see how shallow she was, Stephanie wondered achingly, watching the way Susy curved her fingers round his arm, stroking their painted tips along the soft fabric of his shirt.

As she watched them, something seemed to happen to Stephanie's nervous system. Her stomach clenched as tightly as though the muscles had seized up, waves of pain surging to every nerve ending. Unconsciously, her fingers curled into her palms and then, as Jake bent his head and lightly kissed Susy on the cheek, her taut muscles relaxed into an explosion of nausea. Fortunately, the phone rang, distracting her attention, and, as Jake led Susy into his office and closed the door behind them, Stephanie reached for the phone, trying to control her shaking body. The phone call dealt with, she subsided into her chair.

'Hey, what's the matter with you?' the chirpy voice of one of the other secretaries enquired in concern. 'You look as though you've suddenly gone into shock. You're as pale as a ghost. Are you ill?'

Was she? Feverishly Stephanie leapt at the explanation. Of course, that was it, she must have picked up some sort of bug; that would explain the tearing pains in her stomach and the acute feeling of nausea as well as the waves of heat burning through her veins. Suddenly, her head was pounding, her whole body in the grip of a terrible weakness that made it impossible for her to do anything more than simply stay in her chair.

'I think I must be,' Stephanie admitted, too confused even to marital her thoughts properly.

'You'd better go home.' The other girl was obviously concerned. 'I've never seen you like this, Stephanie. You always seem so cool and in control. Look, I'll ring for a taxi, shall I? Where's Jake . . .?'

'No . . . don't disturb him,' Stephanie was about to say, not wanting either Jake or Susy to witness her humiliating disability, but the door to Jake's office was opening, and he stepped out, Susy clinging to his arm. Both of them were laughing and, on another acute wave of nausea, Stephanie saw that his mouth was slightly stained with Susy's lipstick. The vividness of the mental picture she had of them kissing was accompanied by another tearing pain, and it didn't need Jessie's worried, 'Jake, she's ill' to draw Jake's attention to her milk-white face.

'Stephanie?'

'I think I must have picked up a bug,' she groaned huskily. 'Jake, if you don't mind, I think I'd better go home . . .'

'Of course Jake doesn't mind, do you darling?' Susy murmured throatily. 'You weren't planning to come back this afternoon, were you?'

Stephanie saw him glance at his watch and frown. 'Jessie, ring for a cab, will you?' he instructed tersely. 'Susy, I'd better take Stephanie home. I'll meet you at the Savoy as soon as I can . . .'

Stephanie couldn't have said which of them was the more shocked. Susy burst into immediate and angry argument. 'Jake, for goodness sake, why do you have to take her home . . .? She'll be perfectly all right in the taxi . . . If you're so worried about her, let . . . let this other girl go with her.'

'Jessie is someone else's secretary, and I can hardly commandeer her without his permission, neither can I let Stephanie go home alone. Judging by the state of her, I doubt whether any taxi driver would permit her in his cab unescorted.'

'But our lunch date . . .'

'I'll be there as soon as I can. Jessie, ring for that taxi, will you?'

He spoke in a tone that brooked no further argument, and, although Stephanie was aware of the killing glance Susy gave her, she felt too weak to care. There was something blissfully comforting about having Jake take charge, and already her queasy stomach seemed to be settling slightly, although she still felt dreadfully weak.

Jake didn't wait for the taxi to arrive, decidng instead that they would leave straight away.

Once she was safely installed in his car, Stephanie opened the window slightly.

'What's that for?' Jake asked, 'and don't tell me "fresh air"—at this time of the day, all you're likely to inhale is petrol and diesel fumes.'

'I'll give you advance warning if I think I'm going to be sick,' Stephanie told him shakily, adding, 'Jake, there was really no need for you to do this. I could have gone home on my own.'

'Why did you come in if you weren't feeling well?'

She frowned. His voice was perfectly cool, and yet she sensed beneath it a tension that she couldn't understand.

'I . . . I felt fine this morning . . .'

'Until Susy arrived, I suspect,' Jake agreed, briefly glancing at her. What she saw in his grey eyes made her own widen and darken.

'Well?' Jake queried. 'Am I right . . .?'

'I did start to feel ill after Susy had arrived,' Stephanie agreed unsteadily, not sure where his questions were leading, or why he should be subjecting her to such an intense scrutiny.

'Rather a violent reaction to someone you barely know, wouldn't you say?'

Stephanie frowned. Her nausea seemed to have retreated and her brain was starting to function properly once again.

'Jake, I wasn't sick because of Susy,' she protested. Surely he couldn't really think that? 'It was just coincidence that I should start feeling ill so soon after she arrived.'

'Was it?' He asked the question drily. 'On your own admission, you were feeling fine this morning, and yet, within seconds of Susy's arrival, you were ill enough for me to either have to take you home or feature as the sort of unfeeling monster of a boss any self-respecting trade union would love.'

'Jake . . .' Stephanie felt as cold now as she had felt hot before. 'Jake, please. I don't know what this is all about, but . . .'

'Don't you?' Jake cut in curtly. 'Tell me one thing then, Stephanie. How do you feel now?'

'Now?' She glanced at him in bewilderment, and then said uncertainly, 'Well, I feel much better actually.'

Jake looked at her grimly. 'Now tell me again that your sickness had nothing to do with Susy . . .'

Stephanie opened her mouth to protest, and then said shakily, 'She was wearing a very strong perfume, it could have been that . . .'

'An allergic reaction, you mean?' Jake's smile was cynically mocking. 'Personally, I found it very . . . erotic . . .'

'Yes, so I noticed.' Stephanie couldn't keep the observation back. They were right outside her block of flats, and Jake stopped the car, grasping her forearms and turning her towards him before she could move. 'And just what do you mean by that?' he asked softly.

Stephanie tried to shrug and appear unconcerned.

'Nothing, apart from the fact that it was obvious that you had been kissing her . . . If you hadn't wanted anyone to know, you should have made sure you removed all her lipstick before you left your office,' she added waspishly.

'Tell me something, Steph,' Jake asked with unnerving calm, and a look that sent alarm warnings jolting a powerful voltage of lightning along her veins. 'Why should the thought of me kissing Susy have such a traumatic effect on your nervous system?'

Stephanie stared at him, stunned. What was he implying? That she had simply pretended to be ill to get his attention? But no, it was something more than that, something deeper and so highly personal that her mind cringed away instinctively not wanting to explore or analyse his comment.

'It didn't,' she denied, automatically. 'Why should it? No . . .' Hurriedly, she dragged her glance from his. 'No . . . it must have been Susy's perfume . . .'

'Have it your own way.'

He sounded so totally unconvinced by what she was saying that it provoked her into unwary speech. 'Why should the thought of you kissing Susy make me feel sick?' she demanded angrily. 'I know you've been lovers. I'm not totally naive, Jake. I know you don't live the life of a monk, and I accept that . . . that you . . .'

'That I have sexual needs that have to be satisfied,' he finished contemptuously for her, 'and that you can turn a blind eye to them just as long as they don't intrude into your safe, antiseptic, asexual little world. It's time you stopped burying your head in the ground, Stephanie, and examined just what sort of human being you're becoming.'

'And what sort would you have me become? Someone who goes from man to man, bed to bed, like your precious Susy?' Stephanie didn't know what had happened to her; she was practically screaming at him, and when she saw the satisfied glint in his eyes, she wanted to lash out and scratch felinely at the masculine satisfaction; she wanted to cry and scream, and most of all, she wanted him to take back his accusation about the root cause of her sickness.

'At least she knows what being a woman's all about,' Jake gritted unrelentingly, 'while you . . .'

'I feel sick at the thought of anyone touching me sexually,' Stephanie threw back at him in a high, strained voice. 'Is that so very hard to understand?'

'You weren't sick when I kissed you . . .' Jake reminded her in a soft drawl. 'Only when you thought about me kissing Susy.'

Stephanie stared at him in the confines of the car, appalled by the direction the conversation had taken. 'I don't want to talk about this any more,' she said shakily. 'You're quite wrong, Jake . . . You're trying to impute motives to my responses that just don't belong there. I refuse to believe that I was sick . . .'

'With jealousy?' he finished quietly for her as she thrust open the door.

She paused in mid-flight and stared at him with eyes that were brilliantly green with pain and heightened emotions. 'Jake . . .'

'Why don't you think about it?' he suggested softly.

'I couldn't possibly be jealous of your sexual relationship with Susy,' Stephanie interrupted him heatedly. 'You know I couldn't. I don't think about you in that way. I . . .'

'Think about it,' he advised her, slipping the car into gear. 'Think about it, Stephanie.'

CHAPTER FOUR

IT seemed to Stephanie in the weeks that followed that she thought about precious little else. At work, an atmosphere of uneasy calm prevailed. Although Jake had made no further references to his accusations, they lay at the back of Stephanie's mind like an unbearable weight. In the first flush of anger and anxiety, she had even contemplated handing in her notice, but that impulse had quickly waned. How could she leave? Later, she was to wonder why she hadn't questioned that thought more deeply, but, at the time, she had been so convinced that she was right and Jake was wrong that she had simply accepted it.

Susy was in and out of the office almost constantly, but there had been no repeat of her own initial sickness, which surely proved just how wrong Jake had been.

'I'm taking Susy out to view the riverside property this afternoon,' Jake told her one morning when she went in with his mail. 'She's looking for somewhere in that area. No comment?'

'What am I supposed to say?'

'Did you give any thought at all to what I said to you?' He lifted his eyebrows and watched her across the desk.

Stephanie didn't pretend not to understand.

'Since I haven't been sick since, I thought it hardly necessary,' she returned coolly. 'I realise you seem to think it's high time I got over my . . . what happened, but it simply isn't true that I'm sexually jealous where you're concerned, Jake. We're friends . . . I owe you a great deal, and I'd be sorry to lose our friendship, but . . .'

'But you won't go to bed with me?' He laughed when he saw her expression. 'Don't worry, Steph,' he told her cruelly, 'I doubt I'll ever be that desperate. By the way,' he added almost as an afterthought, 'next weekend I'm taking a couple of days off. I've got a lot to catch up on. I'd like you to come down to Mile End with me if you will. I'll pay you overtime, of course . . .'

It wouldn't be the first time she had visited Mile End, the small Manor House Jake had inherited from his parents, several miles outside Bath, but it was like a slap in the face to hear him talk about 'overtime'; in the past, their working weekends had combined work and friendship and she had treasured them. The old order endeth, she reminded herself, and she didn't have to look far to know why her and Jake's particular order was coming to an end. Gossip and speculation were high in the newspapers that Jake and Susy would marry, and no doubt, once they did, there wouldn't be any place in his life for her.

Not that she wanted a place in the life of the new Jake he was turning into. She barely recognised the man who had been her friend and rescuer in the hard, often sardonic, always watchful person he had turned into.

Where once she would have done everything in

her power to preserve their friendship, now she was aware of putting up invisible barriers between them. Jake had hurt her badly with his accusation that she was jealous of Susy, so badly that she didn't want to analyse why.

There had been other changes in her life as well. Jessie, who she had only known casually before, had become a closer friend. The other girl had called round at the flat to see if she was feeling any better, and they had discovered several interests in common. Jessie lived with her family in Hampstead and Stephanie had enjoyed the couple of evenings she had spent there.

'Doing anything this weekend?' Jessie asked her over lunch.

'No, I've nothing planned.'

'Good, then you'll be able to come to my birthday luncheon party on Sunday.' She pulled a wry face. 'It's an annual event and Mum loves it. The whole tribe will be there, so I'll be glad of your moral support. You will come, won't you?'

On the point of refusing, Stephanie changed her mind. She couldn't turn back the clock to the time when she and Jake had been so close that nothing could come between them, and neither could she live the rest of her life in limbo. She owed it to herself to broaden her horizons, to make more friends.

'I'd love to come,' she said instead. 'What time do you want me there?'

'We normally get going about one, but don't worry about transport, I'll get Keith to come and pick you up.'

Keith was Jessie's elder brother, a pleasant, fair-haired man whom she had met on one of her previous visits.

When Stephanie protested that there was no need, Jessie grinned across at her. 'I daren't tell Keith that. He's threatened that I won't get a birthday present if I don't persuade you to come.'

Stephanie laughed but, on Sunday morning, studying her reflection in her bedroom mirror, she felt the frissons of alarm she always experienced at the thought of meeting new people. She hadn't been able to decide what to wear and, in the end, had opted for her new leather skirt and the matching silk shirt. She was just brushing her hair when Keith arrived, the admiring look he gave her tall, slender figure making her flush faintly.

'I'm sorry, I shouldn't have done that,' he apologised as he opened his car door for her. 'Jessie's always going on about the chauvinistic way men look at women, but you're so very attractive that ...' He broke off as Stephanie blushed again, and grinned. 'You're a very dangerous lady, Stephanie Walters,' he told her softly, 'a rare and highly intoxicating blend of innocence and provocation. I can't understand why there's no permanent man in your life.'

There was a question in the lighthearted comment, but Stephanie chose to ignore it. Much as she liked Jessie's brother, she had no wish to get too involved. She liked him, but as a person, not as a man. She bit her lip, her eyes darkening faintly. She hadn't lied when she had told Jake that she found it impossible to be sexually responsive to his sex, whatever he might choose to think. Keith was nice and she enjoyed his company, but if he made any attempt to touch her . . . She shivered, tensing in her seat.

The luncheon party proved an extremely enjoyable affair. She had already met Jessie's parents and immediate family. Today their large house was bursting with family, friends and neighbours and Stephanie found herself welcomed among them with a warmth that helped to ease the ever-present pain of Jake's defection. In the end, she stayed far longer than she had intended. Long enough to be among the last guests present and when she said that she really must go, Keith immediately offered to take her home.

It was already dark outside and she shivered, imagining the walk from the tube station to her flat. 'That's settled, then,' Keith announced before she could object, 'I'll go and get my car out.'

'Thanks for coming,' Jessie murmured as she went with her to collect her coat, 'and for the terrific present. I'll see you on Monday. Lunch at the usual place?'

'Providing Jake doesn't want to work through,' Stephanie agreed as they walked downstairs together.

'Umm, he is something of an ogre in that respect, isn't he?' Jessie laughed, 'although if you ever wanted a replacement the other secretaries would be standing in line—with me at the head of it. He's so gorgeously sexy isn't he? Just looking at him makes my bones melt.'

Stephanie stiffened slightly, 'I've ... I've never thought of him in that context,' she said quietly, sensing that some response was expected of her.

In other circumstances, she might almost have laughed at Jessie's bemused expression.

'You're putting me on,' the other girl appealed. 'There can't be a woman worthy of the name who *wouldn't* think of him in that context. I can't even walk into his office when he's in there without imagining him without . . .' She broke off as the front door opened and Keith walked in.

'Ready?' he asked.

'Yes, she is, but don't go looking for any dark laybys to park in brother dear,' Jessie teased him. 'Stephanie has the sexiest boss you ever saw and if she's as impervious to *him* as she's just claimed, you haven't a hope.'

They all laughed, and Stephanie hoped that neither of the other two could detect the strain behind her laughter.

It started to drizzle as Keith drove through the centre of London and Stephanie was glad that she had accepted his offer of a lift. Outside her flat, he parked and switched off the engine.

'My mother always told me it was the polite thing to do to make sure my dates got home safely,' he told her with an easy smile as he followed her on to the pavement.

'I'm not your date,' Stephanie pointed out drily.

'No, but that doesn't stop me hoping. I'm not going to push things, Stephanie,' he added gently, as they approached her door, 'so there's no need to look so scared.'

'Was I doing?' She managed a light laugh. 'It must be all those stories Jessie's been telling me about you.'

'If you say so.' He touched her lightly on the arm and, as she tensed automatically, he bent and kissed her lightly on the lips.

'Night, Steph.'

He was gone before she could protest, leaving her stunned by her own lack of response. Although she had recoiled instinctively from him, it had been a reflex action, and the brush of his mouth against hers had produced none of the panic or fear she had expected; and certainly none of the strong emotional reaction Jake's kiss had provoked.

'Jake!' As though her thoughts had somehow conjured him up, as Keith drove off she saw Jake crossing the road and coming towards her.

'Where the hell have you been? I've been ringing all afternoon.' He looked lividly angry, although Stephanie couldn't understand why.

'Where were you?'

'Out,' she responded aggravatingly, 'with a friend.'

'So I saw. Who is he, Stephanie?'

'Does it matter?' Suddenly she was blindingly angry with him, although she couldn't understand why. 'It's the weekend, Jake,' she told him coolly, 'my free time—remember, and I don't have to tell you where I spend it or with whom.'

'Stop trying to be clever, Stephanie.' All at once, he sounded tired and her resistance to him crumbled. She was on such an emotional see-saw these days she hardly knew how she was going to react to him.

'I went to a friend's luncheon party,' she told him in a more natural tone, 'and her brother was kind enough to bring me home.'

'And in repayment for that kindness, you let him kiss you?' His voice was harsh once again. 'I've lost count of the number of times I've brought you home, and yet never once did I get that kind of reward for my kindness.'

'I'm getting wet Jake. I want to go in. I'll see you on Monday.'

From the security of her flat, she watched him walk back to his car, his dark head bare. Only then did she realise that she hadn't asked him why he had come. It wasn't unusual for him to call round to see her during the weekend, or at least it hadn't been until that fatal Friday when he had fractured the security of their relationship for her, and why had he made that comment about Keith kissing her? Depressed to find him once again occupying her thoughts, Stephanie tried to banish him from them, and realised that, for the first time since she had known him, she wasn't looking forward to spending time alone with him, and that she was beginning to dread the subtle sexual pressure that seemed to emanate from him these days. 'Sexy' Jessie had called him, and she had a sudden and very disturbing visual memory of her initial interview with him, before her attack. Then he had come across as intensely sensual, and she had been bemusedly aware of it and of him. Frowning, Stephanie tried to turn her mind to other things.

For two years she had been quite content to think of Jake as a friend, so why, now, were these strange ambivalent feelings surfacing? What were they trying to tell her about herself that she had previously kept hidden?

From wanting to keep his friendship at all costs, she had switched to almost resenting him. Today, when he had questioned her about Keith, watching her with a look in his eyes that told her he knew she was not attracted to the other man, she had felt a deep sense of anger, mingled with a strange primeval fear.

Thoroughly confused, she picked up a paperback book she had bought recently, but, despite its bestseller status, she found she could not get engrossed in it, and she was almost glad when it was eventually time for her to go to bed.

Whether because Jake had elected to take a couple of days off or whether because of a natural increase in work-flow, Stephanie didn't know, but the week following Jessie's luncheon party was so busy that she wasn't able to join her friend for lunch until the Thursday.

'Where on earth have you been all week?' Jessie complained when they were seated opposite one another in their favourite lunchtime haunt. 'It's as though your office has been under siege.'

'We *have* been busy,' Stephanie admitted. 'I haven't been able to leave before seven most evenings.'

'Mmmm . . .' Jessie glanced speculatively at her, 'and I hear on the grapevine that Jake himself has been running you home.'

Stephanie hid her surprise as well as she could, but obviously not well enough because Jessie grinned.

'Oh, believe me, you two are a prime item of gossip in the staff-room. They all think it's very romantic—boss falls for secretary.'

'They're letting their imaginations run away with them,' Stephanie said as lightly as she could, 'and they seem to be forgetting Susy Waldron.'

'Not really. It's just that none of us ever get taken home by our bosses when we work late, but then, none of us seem to have the sort of special relationship with them that you have with Jake.'

It was plain to Stephanie that Jessie would have liked to know more, but she fobbed her off by changing the subject. On the way back to the office she was very thoughtful. Had there always been gossip in the office about her and Jake? After all, he had always taken her home when she worked late, primarily because he knew of her fear of travelling alone, especially during the dark evenings, but because she had never had a close friend among the other girls before she had never dreamed that she and Jake might be the object of speculative gossip.

'Fancy coming round for lunch on Sunday?' Jessie asked her as they entered the office building. 'Mum says you're more than welcome and Keith's pretty keen for you to come as well.'

'No, I'm afraid I . . .' on the point of telling her that she would be spending a working weekend with Jake, Stephanie checked, 'I can't . . .' she finished hesitantly, 'I'm going away for the weekend.'

'Oh. Somewhere nice?'

'Er . . . yes . . . an old schoolfriend,' Stephanie improvised wildly, wishing now when it was too late that she had simply told Jessie the truth.

They parted outside Stephanie's office door, and just as Stephanie was about to open it, Jake strode past her frowning darkly.

'What's got into him?' Jessie enquired once he had gone. 'Whatever he had for lunch obviously didn't agree with him.'

Smiling faintly, Stephanie excused herself. She knew that Jake had been lunching with Susy, and he was back earlier than she had expected.

They were so busy during the afternoon that there was no opportunity for Stephanie to ask Jake about the arrangements for the weekend. At six o'clock when he had finished signing the last letter, he came out and dumped the correspondence on her desk.

'How long will it take you to finish up here?' he asked glancing at his gold watch. The shiny metal glinted under the fluorescent light, fine dark hairs shadowing his sinewy wrist. Jake's hands were lean and long-fingered, the nails clean and well-kept and, to her absolute horror, Stephanie experienced a momentary urge to know their touch against her skin.

'Stephanie?'

The crisp sound of her name jolted her back to normality. 'Er. Half an hour,' she murmured huskily, trying to regain control of her disturbed senses. Jake touching her? Why on earth had that happened?

'I'll drop you off at your flat and then pick you

up in the morning at seven sharp,' Jake continued. 'We should make Mile End easily by late morning that way. Do you want to take this machine?' He tapped her electronic typewriter lightly, raising his eyebrows.

'Yes, I think I will. I'll just get a couple of extra ribbon cartridges for it, and plenty of paper.'

'Does your "friend" know where you're spending the weekend?' For a moment, Stephanie thought he meant Jessie, and said awkwardly, 'No . . . no, I told her I was staying with friends . . . She seems to think . . . that is . . .' she bit her lip and then realised that Jake was frowning. 'Go on,' he instructed sharply, 'we seem to be at cross purposes, but I suspect what you were about to say might prove extremely enlightening. I was referring to your male friend—the one you kiss so gratefully when he takes you home. You, I take it, were referring to Jessie Hargreaves? Now why, I wonder, should you find it necessary to lie to her?'

'I did it without thinking,' Stephanie admitted. 'You see, she was teasing me about . . . about the gossip about you and me—apparently the whole office knows that you take me home when we work late and . . .'

'And she jumped to the wrong conclusion, and to prevent her carrying the tale home to her brother, you decided it might not be a good idea for her to know you were spending the next four days with me.'

Flushing with temper at his sardonic tone and expression, Stephanie said curtly, 'It wasn't like that at all. It never even occurred to me that she might tell Keith . . . I just thought you wouldn't like to think the whole office was gossiping about us.'

'Oh, so it was *my* reputation that was worrying you?' he drawled cynically. 'Then we'll just have to hope you aren't caught out in your lie, won't we?'

Something about his relaxed manner jarred on Stephanie.

'Did you know that . . . that people gossiped about us?' she asked, watching him.

He shrugged powerful shoulders. 'Of course.'

'And it doesn't bother you?'

His laughter angered her. 'What man is ever "bothered" by people thinking he's involved in a sexual relationship with an attractive female, just as long as he's free to be involved in it? How little you know about the male ego, Stephanie.'

Her face flaming, she bent her head to attend to the mail. She had never dreamed that the other members of the staff had gossiped about her relationship with Jake, and she had expected him to be as shocked and surprised as she was herself. Instead, he seemed far from surprised and yes . . . almost amused by her shock.

'Seven o'clock, sharp,' he reminded her briskly as he walked back into his own office, pausing on the threshold to add softly, 'Why didn't you tell this Keith you were spending the weekend with me? Afraid he might object?'

'Keith is a friend and nothing more,' Stephanie retaliated. 'I'm well aware that you think it's high time I had some sort of sexual involvement with a man, Jake, but I refuse to be pushed into a relationship with Keith or any other man that I don't want simply because you think it's what I need. Have you told Susy that you're spending the weekend with me?' she added questioningly.

'She's gone back to the States, today,' he drawled tauntingly, 'but had she been here I would have told her.'

'Because she knows quite well that she has no need to be jealous of me,' Stephanie concluded for him, in a voice that even struck her as oddly bitter.

'Meaning that you're jealous of *her*? Why, Stephanie? Because she shares my bed?'

'Jake, stop this. I don't know what you're trying to do, but I can't continue to work for you if you keep needling me like this,' Stephanie protested thickly, 'You're my boss and my friend . . .'

'So you keep reminding me,' Jake agreed, turning away from her so that she couldn't read his expression, 'but it isn't exactly unknown for friends also to be lovers.' He swung round to watch her betraying reaction portrayed by the rigid tension of her body and he laughed sardonically. 'Come on, Stephanie, it's high time we left.'

As she finished making up the mail, he picked up her typewriter and shouldered open the door. Watching the muscles in his back and shoulders take the strain of the heavy piece of equipment, Stephanie repressed a sharp sensation of pain. It was no use longing for the past. It was over. She had to accept that Jake had changed and that so had their relationship, and she had to learn to live in the present.

She spent the evening preparing for the weekend. She washed her hair and dried it carefully, and then packed her clothes. She had decided on some impulse she couldn't name to take the new separates she had recently bought.

She was just finishing her cup of coffee on Friday morning when she heard Jake's footsteps on the stairs. When she let him in, his eyes raked her sharply, missing nothing of the way her sweater clung to the curves of her breasts, before he completed his leisurely inspection of her. He had never looked at her quite like that before that Stephanie was aware of, and she fought down an immediate panicky response as she turned away to get her case.

'I could use a cup of coffee if there's any going spare,' Jake drawled behind her, as he followed her into her bedroom. 'I overslept and didn't have time for any breakfast. Where's your flatmate?' he added, as he ignored Stephanie's attempts to pick up her case and took it from her.

'Her fiancé's got a week's leave and they're on holiday together.'

'Umm . . . make me that cup of coffee, there's a good girl; it might help me to wake up. I'll take this down to the car.'

When he came back, Stephanie was just pouring the coffee. Jake seemed to fill her tiny kitchen, and instinctively she stepped back from him, wondering as she did so at the curious fluttering sensation in the pit of her stomach.

'Something wrong?'

Stephanie hadn't realised he was studying her so acutely, and she jumped nervously, spilling hot coffee on to her wrist. As she turned to the sink to run cold water over her stinging skin, she was acutely conscious of Jake right behind her. She could smell the faint scent of his soap, and even with her back to him, her mind retained a mental image of him, tall and dark, in the close-fitting black cords he was wearing, the sweater he had on over his shirt adding to the breadth of his shoulders.

'Are you okay?'

'Just a slight scald. I'm always slightly uncoordinated first thing in the morning.'

The grey glance sweeping her slender body had the most odd effect on her nervous system and Stephanie shifted uncomfortably beneath it.

'Did you pack your riding gear?'

Taken slightly aback by the question, Stephanie frowned, 'I thought this was going to be a working weekend?'

'Man cannot live by work alone,' Jake drawled in response.

Often in the past, when she had spent the weekend with him, Stephanie had accompanied Jake to the local riding stables. Riding was a sport they both enjoyed, but for some reason on this occasion Stephanie hadn't thought to add her riding clothes to those she had already packed.

'And you'll need some sort of evening outfit,' Jake added.

'You might have told me that last night,' Stephanie threw the objection at him over her shoulder as she headed for her room. Jake was normally meticulous about warning her what to expect. It wasn't unusual for her to accompany him on business dinners in the evening, but he normally tried to avoid these when he visited his home.

'I forgot.'

Conscious of Jake prowling impatiently round her small sitting room, Stephanie hurriedly reached for a second case, flinging her riding boots and a pair of old cord jeans into the bottom of it before turning to search her wardrobe for a thick jumper. Hastily packing it, she rifled feverishly through the wardrobe for the simple black dress she normally wore for business dinners, and then suddenly remembered that she had taken it to be cleaned. The new suit Annette had coaxed her into buying still hung in its protective plastic wrapper and she was just fingering it absently when Jake strode in.

It wasn't the first time he had been in her room, but today, for some reason, his presence disturbed her. She was conscious of an almost claustrophobic desire to escape and, without pausing to think, she grabbed the plastic wrapper and almost flung the dress into her case. She was on the point of closing it when she remembered the camiknickers she needed to wear under it. Keeping her back to Jake, she pulled open the drawer she had put them in, hastily extracting the pale grey silk satin garment. She was just on the point of putting it in her case when Jake reached out and took it from her suddenly nerveless fingers.

Holding it by the dainty straps, he studied first the grey silk satin and then Stephanie, with a slow intensity that brought a dull surge of colour to her skin.

'I need it to wear under my new evening suit,' Stephanie heard herself saying in a thickly unfamiliar voice. 'Please give it back to me, Jake.'

He was still watching her and continued to do so as he handed the fragile garment over, but the sardonic comment she had been expecting never came, and Jake took the closed case from her without a single word. It wasn't until he had gone out to the car that Stephanie felt able to relax. Released from the tension that had held her in rigid control, her body felt as weak as jelly.

'Ready?'

She had been so wrapped up in her thoughts that she hadn't heard Jake return, and she jumped nervously at the sound of his voice.

'Yes.'

'And Jessie Hargreaves still thinks you're holidaying with friends?'

'Yes,' Stephanie admitted huskily.

'Umm. Well, I hope for the sake of the budding romance between you and her brother that she doesn't put two and two together and make four when she discovers that I'm on holiday too.'

'I didn't lie to her because I didn't want Keith to know,' Stephanie protested as she followed Jake out to his car. 'It was a simple, reflex action . . .'

'Was it, Stephanie? I wonder.'

CHAPTER FIVE

As Jake had predicted, they arrived at Mile End just after eleven o'clock. The house was staffed by a semi-retired married couple, who had originally been with Jake's parents, and who greeted his arrival warmly.

'I've made a light lunch, just as you asked,' Mrs Kettering announced once they were inside, 'and Harry's lit the fire in the library—you said you would be working in there and, although the heating is on, I always think a fire adds real life to a room somehow.' She smiled at Stephanie and added warmly, 'I've put you in your usual room, Miss. Harry will take your cases up for you.'

After lunch when Stephanie followed Jake to his study she could see why he had decided it was necessary to take a couple of days off out of the office to deal with the accumulation of estate work. They worked steadily and harmoniously together until Mrs Kettering brought in a tray of tea at five o'clock, and, as she lifted her head from her dictation pad, Stephanie realised that, for the first time in weeks, they had spent several hours together without coming close to quarrelling, and yet Jake wasn't totally relaxed. She frowned as she noticed the tension of his body as he strode up and down the room, dictating to her.

'What's the matter?' he drawled, breaking off

his dictation to return her scrutiny with interest, 'Have I suddenly sprouted another head?'

'No, only a sour tongue,' Stephanie retaliated. 'I don't know what's got into you lately, Jake; you're like a bear with a sore head ... you're so antagonistic and quarrelsome.'

'Frustration is generally held to have that effect,' he agreed in a laconic drawl that did nothing to lessen the effect of the cool way he studied her body and the way it reacted to his mocking comment, 'which, if you were human enough to suffer from it, you'd know.'

'I hardly think that's a viable explanation,' Stephanie countered, the words out of her mouth before she could stop them, 'to judge by the number of dates you've had with Susy lately, lack of sleep's more likely to be the cause.'

'Just because I've dated Susy doesn't necessarily mean I've made love to her,' Jake returned, his eyes narrowing thoughtfully as he studied her, 'and talking of inexplicable behaviour, what's come over you? You always used to throw up barriers and hide behind them whenever my sex life came under discussion. Now it seems you can't wait to bring it up—and throw it in my face.'

'Perhaps I'm trying to reform you,' Stephanie said it lightly, hoping to deflect him. It didn't work.

'To what purpose? Not jealous of Susy are you, Stephanie?'

'Of course.'

For a moment, her admission threw him. His eyes narrowed again, and he watched her. 'Well, I'm always willing to consider taking you to bed.

In fact I'm beginning to think it's something I should have done months ago,' he added outrageously.

Somehow Stephanie managed to control the wave of hot embarrassment she could feel burning over her skin. She had to pinch herself to remind herself that this was Jake speaking to her; Jake, who had always taken such pains not to embarrass or hurt her in any way; who had always so carefully edited his conversation in the past, knowing how acutely sensitive she was about anything concerning sex.

'When I admitted I was jealous of her, I was referring to her self-possession, her sureness of herself as a woman, and her role in life, not her role in your life,' Stephanie told him.

'You mean you're jealous of her sexuality,' Jake said softly.

Her mouth open to deny his comment, Stephanie closed it again, admitting on a sharp pang of surprise that he was right; although she hadn't known it at the time, that was what she had meant.

'Is it so very surprising?' she asked unsteadily instead. 'I don't exactly enjoy being the way I am, Jake—afraid of all physical and emotional contact with your sex because ... because of what happened, and you haven't exactly been making it easy for me recently.'

'Haven't I?' He came towards her, cupping her jaw in the hard warmth of his palm, his touch surprising her into turning shocked eyes towards his face. 'I should have thought I was making it very easy for you, Stephanie.'

For a moment, Stephanie was held in thrall to the dark mystery of his eyes, absorbing the proximity of him with all her senses. Instinctively, she closed her eyes the better to absorb the male scent of him. With her eyes closed, her other senses became more alert. The touch of his palm and fingers against her skin aroused tiny pulses along her jaw, and she wanted badly to turn her head so that she could taste the male texture of his palm. It was only the sharp, jarring ring of the phone that saved her from making a complete fool of herself, she decided later, when Jake was safely back behind his desk and she was able to conceal her confusion from him by bending her head over her typewriter.

Jake was playing some sort of game with her; she knew that now. There could be no other explanation for his constant reminders of her sexuality. Perhaps his intentions were well-meant and perhaps they weren't. She had no way of knowing with this new Jake whom she didn't recognise and who raised tiny feathers of alarm all along her spine whenever he came within touching distance.

'Okay, that's it for tonight,' Jake announced when he had finished his phone call. He came out from behind his desk and touched Stephanie lightly on the arm; her senses leapt nervously, her immediate reaction to pull away. Almost instantly, his fingers curled round her wrist, his eyes hardening.

'What the devil was that for?' he demanded angrily.

'What?' Nervously, Stephanie touched her dry

lips with her tongue, tension coiling through the pit of her stomach.

'Don't play games with me, Stephanie,' Jake demanded savagely. 'You know exactly what I mean. Why the shudder of distaste when I touched you just then?'

'I don't like being touched—you know that,' she said disdainfully.

She forced herself to meet his eyes. 'I don't even believe I know you any more, Jake. You've changed . . .'

'No . . . but I'm tired of waiting for you to,' Stephanie thought she heard him mutter under his breath before he flung out of the room, his face drawn into a bitter expression of contempt. It was half an hour before she could make her shaky way to her room. Mrs Kettering stopped her on the stairs.

There you are, Miss,' she exclaimed. 'Jake said to tell you that he won't be in for dinner, and that he's arranged for you both to ride first thing in the morning. Eight o'clock downstairs he said to tell you. Would you like to have your dinner in your room, or . . .?'

'In my room will be fine, Mrs Kettering,' Stephanie assured her. Jake had said nothing to her about dining out and she couldn't help feeling that his disappearance had something to do with their conversation in the study.

He had laid the blame for his change of personality at the door of sexual frustration, but Stephanie couldn't believe that. For one thing, there was Susy. Sharply and unexpectedly she had a mental picture of the two of them together,

Jake's body lean and dark, his hands spanning the actress's tiny waist. Sharp shafts of pain lanced through her as she fought to blot out the image, her cheeks flushed with shamed embarrassment. She had never once in the two years she had known him even dreamed of visualising Jake as she just had, *and yet now, suddenly, she found it all too easy to imagine him in the nude*. Shivering she hurried to her room, dropping down into a chair, too numb even to switch on the television. Jake wasn't the only one to change; she was changing herself and in ways that she could hardly bear to admit.

Not even when she lay sleepless in the extremely comfortable bed Mrs Kettering had prepared for her, waiting for the sound of Jake's car, was she prepared to admit the truth. Stubbornly, she clung to the past, telling herself that it was because Jake kept insisting on introducing sexual overtones to their conversations that she had so illuminatingly imagined him as her lover—because it had been her body she had imagined him touching, her body, and not Susy's.

When she eventually heard the car, she roused sufficiently to glance at her watch. It was gone two o'clock. Where had Jake been? He had few friends in the neighbourhood that Stephanie knew of. She would ask him in the morning.

But she overslept slightly, waking to find that it was seven-thirty and that she was going to have to hurry if she was going to go riding with him.

She raced downstairs at ten-past eight, just as he was on the point of leaving. The sound of her booted feet on the stairs stopped him, and he turned in the doorway. Stephanie caught her breath, unwillingly affected by the way his jeans clung to the hard muscles of his thighs, his pose, as he stood in the door, unconsciously arrogant, his black hair ruffled by the breeze through the open door.

'I ... I overslept,' she apologised, blushing furiously when she realised she was stuttering.

'Umm. I thought you'd decided not to come.'

'You know how much I love riding,' Stephanie showed her surprise.

'I also know what a coward you are.' He swung through the door before she could challenge him, and was jumping into the Range Rover parked outside when Stephanie walked out. He opened the passenger door for her and helped her in. Stephanie fastened her seat belt with suddenly clumsy fingers. The late autumn morning was crisp, a faint frost rimed the grass, and in the hollows lay a soft mist.

Above them, the sky was a pale, soft blue with the promise of sunshine later, and she knew a moment's exhilaration such as she had not experienced for a long, long time.

'Ready?' Aware that Jake was looking at her, she nodded her head, bracing herself for the ruts in the road that led down to the farm where the riding stable was.

The owner greeted them cheerfully.

'We've tacked up Emperor for you, Jake,' he said with a smile, 'and Mellisande for you, Stephanie.'

Mellisande was a dainty Arab mare that

Stephanie had ridden before, and she mounted her easily, turning to wait for Jake to mount the huge black stallion prancing skittishly over the cobbles.

As they rode down the lane, birds pecked at the last remnants of the blackberry crop and the mist started to disperse as the sun finally came out. Breathing in lungs full of crisp, sharp air, Stephanie felt a sudden exhilaration, and, as though the sudden tension that ran through her body communicated itself to her mount, Mellisande pranced excitedly.

'Problems?' Jake seemed to tower over her on his mount.

'I think Mellisande's trying to tell me she's tired of simply walking,' Stephanie responded.

'You can let her gallop once we're clear of the lane. We'll go this way.' Jake went first to unlatch the gate, waiting until Stephanie had passed through before closing it. The field in front of them was empty of crops and cattle, and the well-defined path that meandered across it led to a copse and then to the parkland of Mile End.

Feeling the mare prance skittishly beneath her, Stephanie gave her her head. As they raced forward, she heard Jake call out something behind her, but his words were caught by the breeze and so distorted that she couldn't hear exactly what he had said.

Her first intimation that she was no longer in control of Mellisande came when she tried to slow the mare down. Mellisande refused to respond. Up ahead of them, Stephanie could see the tall hedge looming, denuded of leaves now, but fiercely dangerous with its wicked thorns and untidy branches. Helplessly, she sawed on the reins, trying to halt Mellisande's pace, but it was no good. She felt an abrupt jolt as the mare left the ground. The hedge seemed to come racing up to meet her. Behind her, she heard Jake swear and then call out, 'Kick your feet free, Stephanie, and hold on!'

She tried to do as he instructed, and managed to get her feet free, but even so she couldn't keep her balance. As Mellisande cleared the hedge, she felt herself falling, the contact with the frost-hardened ground knocking all the breath from her lungs.

Too shocked and numb to move, she was conscious of Jake dismounting beside her. She tried to roll over and groaned as knives of pain tore through her tender muscles.

'Lie still.' The command was snapped out, and Jake knelt beside her, his hand moving swiftly and clinically over her body. As he touched her, Stephanie felt a curious heat invade her bones. It seemed to radiate out from where he touched her, burning every nerve ending. She groaned a protest as Jake turned her over to lie on her back, shivering with a shock that had more to do with the effect his touch had on her than her actual fall.

Once again, he ran his hands over her, touching her lightly and impersonally, hesitating only when he reached her ribs and his fingers accidentally brushed against the curve of her breast.

'Stephanie?' His voice sounded rough and

unfamiliar, and Stephanie opened the eyes she
had closed when the heat of his touch jolted
through her body.

'How do you feel?'

'Bruised,' she managed semi-humorously. She
struggled to sit up, but he wouldn't let her.

'Lie still for a few minutes; you don't seem to
have broken anything.'

'What about Mellisande?'

'She's probably half way back to her stable by
now. Do you feel well enough to ride back to
Mile End in front of me on Emperor or would
you prefer to stay here until I can bring the
Range Rover?'

'I'll stay here,' Stephanie told him, shuddering
about the thought of the ride back to the house.
Now that the initial shock was over, every bone
in her body was protesting.

'It serves you right,' Jake told her unsym-
pathetically, 'I warned you not to go dashing
off like that, but you ignored me.'

'I didn't hear you,' Stephanie confessed,
struggling to sit up again. The movement
brought a wince of pain to her lips, and she was
staggered to see the white line of anger etched
round Jake's mouth. Nothing in his light, almost
laconic voice had prepared her for it.

'Jake?'

'Lie still,' he told her curtly. 'I'll be back just
as soon as I can.'

With one hand he pushed away the fingers she
hadn't realised she had clasped round his arm,
and a dull flush of colour spread over her skin.
For some reason, her heart was thudding

unevenly, and the warm male scent of Jake's skin made her want to reach out and touch him. She wanted to be held close to the warmth of his body, her head cradled against his shoulder, his hands touching her, but not with the clinical detachment she had experienced earlier.

'Stephanie, is something wrong?'

'Nothing that a hot bath and a rub down with liniment won't cure,' she joked as he stood up. She couldn't let him guess how much she had craved his tenderness, or how much she had wanted him to touch her as a friend . . .

A friend? Her mind taunted her as he mounted Emperor and rode away. Didn't she mean as a *lover*? Wasn't that how she had wanted Jake to touch her; not as a friend, but as a lover?

She was still groggy from her fall, she reasoned with herself; it was only natural that she should crave the comfort of another human being's proximity. Anyone would have done, and yet, when Jake drove up in the Range Rover fifteen minutes later, even though she knew she could have hobbled to him, she let him come to her and lift her in his arms, automatically turning her face into his shoulder and closing her eyes as she savoured the warm heat of it.

'Stephanie, don't faint on me now,' he warned, as he opened the Range Rover door.

'I'm not fainting,' her voice sounded huskily unfamiliar and equally unfamiliar was the sensation of wanting to stay close to him, even to the extent of wanting to cling physically to him as he placed her on the back seat of the vehicle.

'Umm . . . I think I'd better get Dr Jenson to

look at you,' was Jake's dry response as he closed
the door. 'I'm not sure that you're not suffering
from concussion.'

He turned round to look at her and Stephanie
opened her eyes. He was so close that she could
see the tiny lines that fanned out from his eyes
and she let her glance drift across his face until,
unaccountably, it rested on his mouth. Why had
she never noticed before how enticingly masculine
his mouth was with that firm, almost hard, upper
lip and the full, decidedly sensual lower one? Her
own lips parted as she stared dazedly up at him.
What would it be like to be kissed by Jake with
real passion; to know the fierce intensity of his
desire? A tiny sound caught in her throat, and,
from a distance, she heard Jake mutter fiercely,
'For God's sake, don't look at me that way.'

'What way, Jake?' she wanted to ask, but a
great wave of tiredness washed over her and she
gave herself up to it. Later, she could delve more
deeply into the unexpectedness of the sensations
coursing through her; the sudden tingling
awareness that reached out to every part of her
body.

When they got to the house, he lifted her out of
the Range Rover and carried her inside and up to
her room.

'Call Dr Jenson,' he instructed Mrs Kettering
over his shoulder. 'I think she might be suffering
from concussion.'

Stephanie wanted to protest that she wasn't,
but everything was far too muzzy and the next
thing she knew was that the doctor was there,
examining her with a thorough gentleness before

pronouncing that Jake's assessment had probably been quite correct.

'Nothing to worry about,' he told Stephanie calmly. 'I'll leave Mrs Kettering something that will help you to sleep and then, in the morning, Jake, if she's no better, we'll think again.'

'I'm perfectly all right,' Stephanie wanted to protest, but the doctor was already leaving. Jake threw her a frowning glance over his shoulder, and she stared mutinously back. Once the doctor had gone, she would tell Jake that there was nothing wrong with her and that she was getting up. Concussion . . .

The next thing she knew was that Mrs Kettering was standing beside her bed, proffering a glass of water and some tablets. 'They'll help you to sleep,' she told Stephanie when she looked doubtfully at them. 'Dr Jenson thinks you're suffering more from shock than concussion, but he wants you to rest.'

Stephanie wanted to refuse them, but weakly she took them and drank the water. Where was Jake? Was he furious with her? He had brought her here to work, not to loll about in bed.

The next time she woke up it was dark. She had been deeply asleep, and she tensed as she saw someone move in the shadows of the room.

'Hungry?'

She blinked, as she recognised Jake's voice. How long had he been sitting there in that chair watching her?

'How long have I been asleep?' she asked him croakily. 'It's gone dark.'

'It's nearly eleven o'clock,' Jake responded

wryly, 'Would you like something to eat?'

Stephanie shook her head.

'Not feeling sick, are you?' Jake queried sharply, coming closer to the bed and leaning towards her. The sharp, musky male scent of his body was disturbingly arousing. Sensations Stephanie hadn't known existed stormed through her body leaving her disorientated. Her eyes widened as her glance slid towards his mouth. Only this morning, she had noticed how sensual it was and had wondered what it would feel like against hers, kissing her with passion and not anger.

'Stephanie, don't look at me like that,' Jake muttered in a tortured voice that jolted her into brief awareness of what she was doing, but that awareness retreated beneath the wave of sexual response his voice conjured up and without moving her gaze ftom his mouth, Stephanie whispered huskily, 'Like what?'

'Like you want to feel my mouth on yours, like this,' Jake responded in a thick, almost drugged tone, lowering his head until his breath brushed the tendrils of hair curling round her temples.

Stephanie closed her eyes instinctively, her whole body trembling in anticipation. She did want Jake to kiss her, she acknowledged; she wanted it with a fierce intensity that at any other time would have terrified her, but now, all she was aware of was that her body was already melting in satisfied anticipation and that when Jake lifted her arms, it seemed the most natural thing in the world to lock them behind his head as she arched up in response to the heat of his hands against her back, lifting her off the bed and against his body, teasing brief kisses against her mouth as he did so.

'Jake.' His name was a moaned sound that he captured with his mouth, his tongue forcing her to yield to the powerful surge of emotion she felt consuming them both. She had no will, no thought, no purpose in life, save for the satisfaction of this aching hunger that Jake seemed to feed inside her. When his hand slipped the strap of her nightdress off her shoulder, her skin seemed to burn beneath his touch. She yielded herself to him in a tide of bone-melting urgency, no thought in her mind other than her compelling need to lose herself in the sensations he was arousing. When his hand cupped her breast, she shuddered in response, opening dazed eyes to meet the darkly grey glitter of his.

'Stephanie, kiss me . . . touch me.' The thick, aching mutter was so unlike the voice he normally used that she was too bemused to protest when he tore impatiently at the buttons on his shirt, sliding her hand inside it. Beneath her fingers, she could feel the crispness of his body hair. His skin felt hot and moist, his heart thudding irregularly into her palm. Touching him generated an excitement that increased her pulse rate until it matched the heavy thud of his heart, and *she* was the one who unfastened the remaining buttons on his shirt, pressing both hands against his skin, savouring the sensation of feeling it beneath her own.

Distantly, she was aware of Jake muttering something, as his body shuddered against hers, just as she was aware of the cool night air against her skin as he slid the other strap down her shoulder until he had exposed both breasts.

'Stephanie.' Her hands were lifted from their resting place against his chest and so great was her feeling of loss that she was hardly aware of Jake sliding her straps over her arms.

'Jake, I want to touch you,' she protested, surprised to hear herself saying words which part of her brain told her she should never have uttered, but why not? She *did* want to touch him, so badly that it was almost a fever in her blood. She bent her head and touched her tongue to the hollow of his throat, tasting the salty male texture of his skin. Beneath his breath, Jake groaned, his throat arching as it invited her hesitant touch. Under her tentative exploration, his body tensed, his muscles rigid and then, suddenly, with an explosion of sound, he pulled her down on to the bed beside him, his thumb strokingly caressing over her nipple, making it grow hard and taut as his mouth captured her startled cry of protest and his tongue explored deeply into hers.

Waves of pleasure beat fiercely through her body, making her want to arch and cling, to cry out with pleasure and to beg for more; as she arched her body closer to Jake's Stephanie dislodged the glass Mrs Kettering had left on the table beside the bed. The sound it made as it crashed to the floor broke through the half-hypnotic trance Jake's touch had evoked and reality flooded in.

'Jake!' At first, her horrified protest had no effect. His mouth had released hers in favour of the satiny skin of her throat and, as Stephanie tensed beneath him, his lips moved downward until they were tasting the creamy sweetness of her breast.

A shocked gasp stifled in her throat as her body responded against her will to the delicate touch of his tongue as it explored the deep rose-pink aureole of flesh that crowned her breast, and then, when she started to shiver with a reaction compounded of sexual excitement and self-revulsion, Jake lifted his head to study her flushed face and fever-bright eyes.

With her eyes accustomed to the moonlight, Stephanie could see the dark arrowing of hair matting his chest, and remembered how she had stroked her fingertips through it, before kissing the moist male skin. What on earth had possessed her?

'Jake, please, you must leave,' she told him, her voice husky with pain and self-contempt. 'I don't know what happened, but . . .'

'Don't you, Stephanie?' he was already on his feet, tucking the shirt back inside his jeans, his voice dry and cold. 'Would you like me to tell you?'

He must have seen her flinch because he laughed sardonically. 'You wanted me, Stephanie,' he told her. 'You looked at me and wanted to know what I would be like as a lover. You looked at my mouth as though you couldn't wait to find out how it would feel against your skin.'

'No . . .' Her denial was a tortured moan. 'No . . . I was concussed . . . I didn't know what I was doing . . .'

'You mean that frightened child who controls you didn't know what she was doing,' Jake interrupted coolly. 'The woman in you knew exactly what she was doing.'

'Jake, please ... I know you must be missing Susy, but I won't ... I won't be used as a substitute. I ...'

'You know *nothing*, Stephanie,' Jake told her, as he moved away from the bed, fastening his shirt, 'nothing at all, because you won't let yourself know, and before you start allocating the blame, remember you were the one who invited me. I merely responded as any male would to such a blatant female invitation.'

Although she turned away from him, Stephanie was acutely aware of the exact moment he left her room and, in spite of knowing that she should be relieved that he had gone, part of her wanted him to stay; part of her wanted him next to her, his arms round her, his heart beating reassuringly beneath her cheek, his hands and mouth caressing her body ...

Trembling, she tried to compose herself to sleep. She had always thought that when and if she ever experienced physical desire it would only be because she was in love. Never, ever, had she imagined experiencing those feelings for Jake. *Because she had always known that it would be dangerous to love Jake, an inner voice told her*; Jake was not a man who gave anything of himself easily, and so she had opted for friendship, knowing that she would never have his love. Was that it? Of course not. Not until he had started making her aware of himself had she ever thought of Jake in any remotely sexual way. Had she? Unwillingly, Stephanie remembered their initial interview, and how she had felt, how she had responded against her will to the magnetic maleness of him, but all that had gone after she had been attacked, and it had never come back ... Until now. She loved him? Oh, but she couldn't! She had seen what happened to the women who loved him; he grew bored with them.

Like a bolt of lightning, the truth struck her. She had fallen for Jake almost on sight but, after the attack, shock and self-preservation had combined to make her turn Jake from a potentially dangerous threat into a safe 'friend'. Could Jake himself have known this? He couldn't know that she had been foolish enough to fall in love with him, otherwise he would never have made love to her as he had, Stephanie reassured herself. No, Jake had probably made love to her in some misguided attempt to break down the barriers she had raised against his sex. He would never deliberately hurt her by playing on her feelings for him, she was sure of that. No, he didn't know she loved him. How could he? She hadn't known herself until tonight, and he must not know. He must *never* know. Somehow, when she next met him, it must be as the cool, efficient secretary she had always been and not the woman who had turned to melting compliance in his arms.

CHAPTER SIX

STEPHANIE was already awake the following morning when the doctor arrived. He was shown up to her room by Mrs Kettering and Stephanie forced down her aching feeling of disappointment because she wasn't Jake as she responded to her concerned enquiries.

'Well now, let's have a look at you,' the doctor said cheerfully. Stephanie remained patiently still whilst he completed his examination.

'Nothing much wrong there,' he announced, once he had finished, 'slight temperature, but that could be anything; certainly there aren't any signs of concussion this morning. Sleep well last night, did you?' He had his finger over Stephanie's pulse and she knew he must have registered the hurried acceleration although he made no comment when she responded lightly, 'Yes, quite well.'

'Umm. No after-effects from the pills I left? No muzziness, or drowsiness? Some people sometimes complain that they affect them that way.'

'Nothing,' Stephanie responded quietly, wondering if any of his patients had ever complained that they left them completely without inhibitions because that was what had happened to her. Last night, her fear of sexual contact had simply melted away and, for the first time in her adult

98

life, she had experienced the full force of a sexual magnetism so intense that she simply had not been able to resist it. But it wasn't simply sexual magnetism that had taken her into Jake's arms; she had wanted to be there with a fierce need whose roots lay within herself.

'Stay in bed this morning and rest,' the doctor advised as he stood up.

'I'm here to work,' Stephanie protested.

'And you'll work all the better for resting this morning. That was a nasty tumble you took and, although nothing's broken, it will be quite some time before your body's recovered from the shock.'

Stephanie suspected that he might have been right if her body hadn't had another and even more potent shock to contend with.

Once they had gone, she made her way to her bathroom, wincing as her bruised muscles protested. When she had bathed and dried herself, she opened the door to discover that Mrs Kettering was just on the point of entering her room, carrying a large tray.

'I've brought you your breakfast,' she told Stephanie with a smile, 'and Dr Jenson says I'm to make sure you don't get up until after lunch.'

'I'm causing you an awful lot of extra work,' Stephanie apologised, 'and Jake must be furious. I know he had a great deal to get through this weekend.'

'Now, don't start worrying about that. It's no extra work at all to bring a tray upstairs and, as for Jake, he's gone out.'

It was one thing to tell herself last night that

she must not allow Jake to guess how she felt
about him. It was quite another this morning to
deal with the misery she felt on learning that he
had gone out without coming to see her. But why
should he? He must be as eager to forget what
had happened last night as she was, and perhaps,
by going out, he was trying to tell her that the
incident was closed.

A morning in bed with nothing to do but
analyse her thoughts and emotions was scarcely
the best medicine for her newly discovered
complaint, Stephanie thought wryly. For one
thing, it made her remember small incidents that
had slipped to the back of her mind but which
she was now remembering with unwanted clarity.
There had been the way Jake had pulled away
from her on several occasions recently, whenever
she had touched him accidentally. Because she
was the one who normally avoided the slightest
physical contact she had not given his actions a
great deal of thought, but now she did. In the
early days of their friendship, Jake had often
touched her in a friendly way, until he realised
how much she hated it, but he had never before
actually avoided physical contact with her. What
was she to make of that?

She started to tremble violently as one
explanation presented itself to her, and she was
shivering fitfully when Mrs Kettering came in
with a cup of coffee.

'Cold?' the older woman exclaimed with some
concern. 'I'll get Harry to come and light your
fire for you.'

'No . . . no, I'm fine really,' Stephanie

responded. 'Just someone walking over my grave.'

No, not her grave, she thought dismally when Mrs Kettering had gone, but the grave of her friendship with Jake. There had been changes in him that she had been too blind to see; the friendship she had treasured so much had started to die a long time ago, but she had refused to see it; had refused to acknowledge that Jake was growing weary of the role she had given him. In the distance, Stephanie heard a phone ring, and then silence as someone answered it. Half an hour later, when Mrs Kettering returned for her cup, she said worriedly, 'There's been a phone call for Jake from New York, a Miss Waldron. She wanted to know where he was, but I couldn't tell her.'

'Did she say she'd ring back?' Stephanie asked, trying to ignore the white-hot knives of jealousy slicing through her nerves.

'No, she wants him to ring her. Left a number. I've written it down on the pad in the library. Me and Harry have been saying for some time that we'd like to see him settled down—this house is crying out for a family to bring it to life, but I doubt that Mile End would see much of him if he marries that one. A regular high flyer she is and no mistake.'

'Have you ever met her?' Stephanie asked, trying to sound unconcerned, but in reality filled with a bitterly intense jealousy. Had Jake ever brought Susy here? Perhaps made love to her in the privacy of the large, masculine bedroom she had only been in once when Jake had asked her to bring some papers up from the library.

'No, but what I've read about her's enough,' Mrs Kettering said darkly. 'You're looking pale,' she added with concern as she looked at Stephanie. 'Perhaps you ought to stay in bed for the rest of the day. No sense in getting up and exhausting yourself for no purpose. Jake said he didn't know when he'd get back.'

'No, I'm getting up after lunch,' Stephanie told her, not knowing whether to feel glad or sorry that Jake might not be there. On the one hand, she felt a fierce longing to see him again; a longing so intense that she didn't know how she was going to stop herself from reaching out to touch him, and yet, on the other, she felt a revulsion against looking at him, and seeing in his eyes the cold rejection she was sure there would be there.

In the end, she spent the afternoon finishing the dictation Jake had given her the day before and tidying out the files he kept at Mile End. It was growing dusk when Mrs Kettering came in to protest that she had done enough.

'Jake said not to make any plans for dinner, so it looks as if he won't be coming back,' she added. 'I dare say he feels guilty,' she added, startling a betraying gasp from Stephanie's half-parted lips. 'After all,' Mrs Kettering continued, 'if you hadn't gone riding with him, you wouldn't have had your accident, would you?'

'Oh, that wasn't Jake's fault,' Stephanie assured her, hoping that the housekeeper hadn't noticed her swift change of colour or the betraying tremble of her body. For a moment, she had thought Mrs Kettering had known about last night. Her own guilty conscience at work, Stephanie thought wryly. 'If Jake isn't coming back for dinner, I think I'll have an early night.'

'A good idea,' Mrs Kettering approved. 'Now what would you like to eat?'

Mile End was a lovely house, but very lonely without Jake, Stephanie admitted when she eventually prepared for bed. It was only ten o'clock, but her bruised body was quite glad of the comfort of her warm bed. Where was Jake? And who was he with? Downstairs she heard the phone ring and wondered if it was Susy, and if the other woman shared her gnawing jealousy at his absence.

It was with a resolve to face Jake as though nothing had happened that Stephanie went downstairs the following morning. He was already in the breakfast room dressed casually in black cords and a black cotton shirt open at the throat, when she walked in. The morning sun showed lines of tiredness and strain on his face that she hadn't noticed before, a certain grimness to his mouth that caught at her heart. When he saw her, he raised his eyebrows and drawled, 'Do you think you're well enough to be down here?'

'Perfectly,' Stephanie responded with a crispness which she hoped deceived him better than it did her. 'After all, I was working yesterday afternoon. Did Mrs Kettering tell you that Susy called?'

'She did mention it, yes. Stephanie, I want to talk to you about the other night.'

She had been on the point of reaching for the coffee pot and her body tensed, her hand arrested in its movement.

'There's nothing to talk about,' she managed at last. 'I realise that ... that you were probably missing Susy, and that I was there, and that's all there is to say about it.'

He was silent for so long that Stephanie had to look at him. His eyes, narrowed faintly against the sun, appraised her tense features, giving nothing away about his own feelings. 'Very well,' he said at last, 'if that's the way you want to play it. By the way,' he added, 'dinner this evening will be a formal "do". You did bring a dress, didn't you?'

'Yes.' Stephanie had to look away as she remembered the way he had held up the camiknickers that went with her new evening dress, his fingers caressing the satin as though they enjoyed the tactile experience.

'Are you sure you feel up to working today?' His concern was patently only that of an employer and Stephanie felt an irrational pulsation of anger. It wasn't his fault that, instead of his cool enquiry, she would rather have had the warmth of his arms around her and the heat of his kisses to melt away the residual ache in her bones.

'Perfectly,' she told him, buttering a slice of toast. 'What time do you want to start? There must be quite a backlog with losing yesterday.'

'Sometimes I wonder if you're human at all,' he drawled, getting up and standing over her. 'The perfect, efficient secretary, programmed to make all the right responses, that's you isn't it, Stephanie?'

The words were meant to hurt and they did, leaving her frantically trying to suppress her tears as he walked out of the breakfast room and left her alone.

When she eventually joined him in the library, he made no reference to his behaviour. Several bulky files were on his desk and, as soon as Stephanie was sitting down, he started to dictate. The day was cold again, but a fire flickered warmly in the old-fashioned hearth, throwing shadows across Jake's face that gave it an oddly gaunt expression. He must be losing weight, Stephanie thought, frowning slightly as she noticed the waistband of his jeans was loose, and then a heavy tide of colour swept up under her skin as she remembered how she had touched and kissed him, and her whole body trembled with feverish need to repeat the experience.

'Stephanie? Stephanie, are you all right . . .?'

Half-dazed by the power of her emotions, Stephanie realised that Jake had come round the desk to stand beside her, and that he was bending towards her, his hand on the back of her chair. 'Look, if you're not feeling up to this . . .' His presence; the musky, male scent of his body and her own powerfully aroused emotions combined to bemuse her. There was nothing wrong with her that his kisses couldn't cure, Stephanie knew, and yet she made no attempt to reassure him.

'Stephanie, damn you, what's wrong?' His hand left the back of her chair to circle her throat, his thumb tilting her jaw so that he looked down into her eyes.

'Do you feel faint? Are you in pain? Stephanie, for God's sake.' The growled imprecation reached through the fog of desire engulfing her, her body responding to its roughly masculine tones. Nervously, Stephanie touched her tongue to her lips, dimly hearing the taut sound that echoed from Jake's throat in response, and then, just as he bent towards her, the phone started to ring.

In the handful of seconds it took Stephanie to jolt back into an awareness of reality, Jake had left her side and was picking up the receiver, his eyebrows drawn together in a heavy frown, his eyes glittering over her face and body as he held the phone. And then, suddenly, his expression changed. He swung away from her, his voice warm with open pleasure as he said huskily, 'Susy, you know I'm always pleased to hear from you, but hang on just a minute.'

His hand covered the receiver, and he turned back to Stephanie. 'If you don't mind, I'd prefer to take this call in private.'

Somehow she managed to get out of the library, her entire body a mass of aching pain. She couldn't comprehend that only seconds ago she had felt so vitally attuned to Jake that her mouth had already been anticipating his kiss. Why couldn't she accept that she was simply a substitute for Susy, and that any desire he might feel for her sprang only from the fact that he was missing the other girl?

She waited for half an hour before going back into the library. When she did so, Jake was seated behind his desk. He looked up and glanced coolly at her as she walked in and sat down, her pencil poised above her pad.

'Ready?'

It was gone six o'clock before she finally finished all the dictation Jake had given her, her mind and body both bruised and aching with pain.

It was only as she went upstairs that she remembered the formal dinner. Jake had made no mention to her of his other guests, and she could only presume that they were local people who had perhaps known his parents. She knew that in the past Jake had toyed with the idea of opening a branch of the partnership locally, but, as far as she knew, this was still only a 'maybe'. Perhaps tonight's dinner had some bearing on that.

Tired to the point where all she really wanted was sleep, Stephanie showered and washed her hair, twisting it up into a complicated pleat. Not wanting to crease her new outfit, she sat in front of the mirror in her camiknickers to do her makeup. The slight tan she had gained during the summer gave her legs enough colour for her not to need tights or stockings, and, as she applied deft touches of eyeshadow to enhance the colour and size of her eyes, she tried not to look at the provocative way the spotted net cups of her underwear outlined her breasts. The silk satin clung lovingly to every curve of her body, the back dipping down to the base of her spine. Never would she have chosen such an article of clothing herself, and several times she was tempted to take it off. Only the knowledge that if she did she would not be able to wear a bra stopped her, and when she had finally finished applying her makeup she was forced to acknowledge that the natural flush of colour staining her cheeks owed its presence almost entirely to her own unease with what she was wearing.

Once she had dressed in her evening suit, she felt a little happier. The high neckline at the front was reassuringly formal, although she hadn't realised how restricting the straight skirt would be when she walked. A final glance in the mirror assured her that her appearance was as elegantly formal as it should be, and then she was on her way downstairs.

Jake, as she had expected, was already in the drawing room, standing in front of the fire. Evening clothes suited him, and, although she had seen him in them on countless occasions before, this was the first time she had been so intensely aware of him. Her pulses fluttered warningly as she crossed the room, accepting the glass of sherry he poured for her.

'What time are the others expected?' she asked, her eyes drawn against her will to the deft movements of his fingers as he replaced the crystal stopper in the decanter.

'There are no others.'

'No others . . . but you said we were dining formally . . .'

'That's right. So we are,' Jake agreed, flicking back his cuff to glance at his watch. 'Mrs Kettering warned me that the cheese soufflé she's prepared doesn't like to be kept waiting, so if you're ready . . .'

Half a dozen questions clamoured for answers, but, before she could ask even a single one of them, Stephanie was reduced to suffocating silence by the warm pressure of Jake's hand against the small of her back. Her skin seemed to tingle where he touched it, an intense heat spreading out from his fingers to every centimetre of her skin.

The dining room of Mile End was decorated in a mixture of reds and gold. Silverware and crystal gleamed softly on the polished table and Stephanie had the bemused feeling that she had suddenly been transported to another world. Why on earth had Jake gone to all this trouble to eat with her? She couldn't count the number of meals she had shared with him, and yet this was the first time they had dined together formally. Why?

The warm pressure of his hand increased as he pulled out her chair for her and, when it was removed, Stephanie felt oddly bereft. Dazedly, she was aware of Jake pouring her a glass of wine and of Mrs Kettering wheeling in a heated food trolley.

'Souffl?' Stephanie was suddenly aware that Mrs Kettering had gone, and nodded her head slowly.

'Jake . . . what is this?' she asked when he had served them both. 'You told me . . . that is, I thought . . . Jake, what's happening to us?' she asked urgently, pushing away her food untouched. 'We were friends, but now . . .'

'You're trying to hold on to something that no longer exists, Stephanie,' he told her brutally.

Yes, we were friends, but, as friendships go, ours involved certain restraints. For instance, we were never friends in the way that two men could have been friends.'

When she opened her mouth to protest, he added sardonically, 'You don't agree? If we had been you wouldn't have objected to my discussing my sex life with you, would you, but, as I recall, that subject was taboo. You didn't even want to acknowledge that I had a sex life, did you?'

'Jake, please . . .' Agitated and upset, Stephanie took a deep gulp of her wine. 'Why are you doing this?'

'Why? You can't spend the rest of your life ignoring subjects you don't like, Stephanie, and, as for tonight, well, let's just say that I'm celebrating the end of one era and the beginning of another.' When he saw her expression, he laughed cynically. 'You don't even know what I mean, do you?'

'The food . . .' Stephanie protested feebly, dragging her eyes away from his. 'Mrs Kettering must have gone to so much trouble . . .'

'And you're so hungry,' he mocked, eyeing her untouched soufflé. 'Very well, then . . . by all means let's eat first and then talk later . . .'

He served her with chicken breast cooked in a rich cream sauce and accompanied by a selection of beautifully prepared vegetables, but Stephanie felt as though she would choke with every mouthful. Her stomach was tense with nervous dread. What was there to talk about? 'An end of an era' Jake had said. Did that mean he was going to fire her? Sick with misery she watched Jake clean his plate, numbly refusing dessert or cheese and biscuits. When Jake reached for the bottle of brandy, she shook her head.

'No, I forgot, you don't like the taste, do you?' he said softly, and for some reason he recapped the bottle without pouring any for himself either.

'Why aren't you having any?' She half stammered the question, seizing on anything that would put off the dreaded moment when they would have to talk.

'Why?' Jake got up and walked towards her, his hands resting on her chair, compelling her to stand up and face him, and give in to the insistent pressure of his fingers round her arm.

'Let's go into the drawing room. We'll talk about it in there.'

Feeling her tension increase with every footstep, Stephanie followed him. The drawing room fire had been lit, and its flames and a single lamp were all that illuminated the gracious room. When she would have chosen one of the chairs beside the fire, Jake drew her down alongside him on the deep settee. Coils of nervous dread writhed through her stomach, the effort of trying to appear cool and composed draining her of every shred of energy.

'Now,' Jake said lightly without releasing her, 'tonight I intend to disabuse you of any ideas you might still have that we are "friends", Stephanie.' He ignored her gasp of pain, and continued evenly. 'When I think of you, I don't so much see a "friend" as a very desirable woman. Would you like to feel what you do to me?' Before she could protest, he had taken her hands and placed them beneath his jacket. Against her palm, she could feel the furious racing of his heart and, when she lifted her head, his eyes glittered back a message of unmistakable desire.

'Jake ...' She said his name hesitantly ... wonderingly, almost. 'And I didn't have a brandy because you don't like the taste of it ... and, besides, you're intoxicating enough.' Stephanie thought she heard him mutter as his hands slid up to cup her face and his mouth descended to fasten compellingly over hers, communicating a depth of hunger that part of her registered as being acutely intense enough for him to feed her own famished senses, hurtling them both dangerously close to complete loss of control.

'Jake ...' Her lips were almost too swollen and tender to form his name when he finally released her. Beneath her palms, his chest rose and fell unevenly, his heartbeat striking against her with hammer blows. If anything, the grey glitter darkening his eyes had intensified, and the mouth, that only that weekend she had recognised as intensely passionate, bore nearly as much evidence of their kiss as her own. Wondering, she reached out and touched it, tracing the male curves, quivering tensely with a mingling of awe and wonder. Fierce hard need tensed his body, his lips parting to touch her finger, his teeth nibbling gently.

'Stephanie.' His hand left her face to pull her own closer to his mouth, his tongue stroking roughly across her palm.

'Stephanie, I want you and you want me, too . . .'

'No . . .'

'Yes. Do you think I haven't seen the way you've been looking at me recently? Do you think I'm immune to it . . .?'

'I haven't been looking at you any differently,' Stephanie lied.

'Oh yes, you have. Whether you're willing to admit it to yourself or not, you've been visualising me as your lover . . .'

'No!' Her sharp protest brought a fiercely heated flare of response to his eyes.

'Yes,' he told her, watching her. She gasped, a long shuddering moan that proved his point more easily than a thousand words as he lifted his head and trailed his tongue down along the curve of her throat. Shivers of pleasure radiated through her body, her skin tormentingly aware of him.

'Now,' he mocked tauntingly. His teeth nipped at her ear, one hand resting on her back while the other traced the shape of her jaw line and teased the arching line of her throat. 'Kiss me, Stephanie. When you walked in here tonight, you looked at me as though you couldn't wait to feel my skin beneath your fingers. Touch me with that wanting now . . . Do it, damn you,' he swore against her ear. 'Prove to me that you've got the courage to be a woman. You want me, Stephanie. Have the guts to admit it.'

His words had a similar effect on her body to his earlier kiss. She was trembling with reaction and a hunger she didn't want to name. The mental pictures conjured up by Jake's words tormented and taunted. Her fingers found the buttons of his shirt; trembled against them, and then withdrew. She closed her eyes as she heard Jake curse and move restlessly. 'There,' he muttered hoarsely, pulling her back against him, her hands crushed against the naked heat of his chest. 'There, does that make it easier for you?' He had thrown off his jacket and unfastened his shirt down to the waist. Dazedly, Stephanie let her gaze drift over the tanned planes of his body, her fingers nervously smoothing the dark tangle of body hair that arrowed sharply down over his flat stomach, stopping only when Jake moaned a harsh protest, trapping her hand against his skin.

'You don't have the faintest idea what you're doing to me, do you?' he demanded rawly. 'Stephanie, Stephanie . . . I've been going mad for the feel and taste of you . . . waiting for just a sign that you were aware of me as a man.'

'Jake . . .'

'Don't talk—not now. I can't even formulate a single, co-ordinated thought right now. I've hungered for this, Stephanie . . . ached for it . . . it's been like a sickness dammed up inside me. Right from the first moment you walked into my office, I knew I wanted you . . . and we would have been lovers, too, if it hadn't been for those . . .' He uttered a word that half-shocked her, and then said tautly, 'I wanted to kill them for what they did to you . . . and God knows how many times I've wanted to kill you these last two years . . . I couldn't even touch you without you flinching away . . .'

'You're touching me now,' Stephanie pointed

out in a husky whisper, more stunned than she wanted him to see by his revelations. Why had she never seen that he wanted her? Because he hadn't allowed her to see. He had cloaked his desire for her in friendship, and not allowed her to see beyond that friendship. Because she hadn't wanted to see. Because she hadn't dared to admit that Jake merely wanted her as he had wanted so many other women and that, once his desire for her was sated, there would be no place in his life for her. Alarm stirred to life inside her. She couldn't let this go any further. But Jake's hand had slipped inside her dress, reaching round to cup her breast over the thin net. His thumb stroked over her nipple and all thoughts of resisting were forgotten.

'I'm touching you now because I know that you want me to,' Jake told her huskily. 'You do want me to, don't you, Stephanie?'

'No ... yes ...' she admitted feebly as his probing thumb brought such exquisite sensations of pleasure coursing through her body she could barely formulate the simple word.

'Let me take this thing off.'

Knowing she should protest and yet somehow unable to do so, Stephanie let him ease the top of her suit over her head before he eased down the zip of her skirt, quickly dispensing with it.

'I'm surprised you bothered to go to all the trouble of telling me to dress formally when this was what you had in mind,' she managed to say dryly when he held her satin-clad body in his arms.

'I knew it was the only way I'd get to see you

in this.' His hands smoothed the satin over the curves of her waist and hips. 'And I wanted to see you in it, Stephanie.' His hands reached up and pulled the securing pins from her hair so that it tumbled down round her shoulders. For one breathless moment, her eyes met Jake's, her body taking fire from what she read there. She had never before had occasion to think of herself as anything even approaching reckless, but she knew in that instant that she was and that she was going to give in to the reckless impulse to be tonight whatever Jake wanted her to be, and to take whatever she could from life without pausing to count the cost or think about tomorrow. As though he knew her thoughts, Jake made a muffled sound somewhere between a groan and a curse, and then his tongue was probing her lips, and they were opening to his touch. Exploration gave way to fierce possession as he fed hungrily on the moist yielding of her mouth, pulling her into the hard curves of his body until they were lying side by side on the settee. The fingers of one hand splayed possessively over her waist, while those of the other tangled in her hair, holding her mouth captive beneath his.

'Touch me, Stephanie,' he insisted hoarsely, when he finally released her lips, his teeth still biting compulsively into their softness, as though he couldn't bear to let her go. 'Feel what you do to me.'

Closing her eyes, Stephanie placed her hands against his skin, absorbing the damp heat of it, feeling the thunder of his heart. Jake groaned, his thumb stroking urgently over her nipple, his hand in her hair, compelling her face into the curve of his shoulder. Her lips touched his skin, registering the shudders of pleasure her touch evoked. She had never dreamed that Jake could lose control like this. She had always known somehow that he would be a skilled lover, but she realised she had visualised him as a remote one, giving pleasure, and taking it, but always remaining aloof, apart. This Jake who moaned her name while his skin turned fever hot beneath her touch; who kissed her with a hunger she couldn't gauge, who trembled when he touched her body, was not the Jake she had visualised. Was he like this with Susy? Jealousy seared through her, burning into her bones, kniving agonisingly through her stomach. She couldn't bear the thought of him touching any other woman. Her fingers curled into his skin, her nails raking lightly against it in mute protest.

'You're driving me mad, do you know that?' Jake's hands slid to her hips, pressing her into the hardness of his thighs, letting her feel the tide of arousal sweeping through him, making her ache with a physical pain she hadn't known was possible.

The firelight threw shadows of gold and red over his skin.

'Tonight I'm going to make love to you, Stephanie. You want me to, don't you?'

Warning bells penetrated the miasma of jealousy and desire enveloping her. If she admitted that she wanted him to make love to her, wouldn't Jake guess that she loved him? Despite all he had said about wanting her, he had

never mentioned love; and then there was Susy
... Susy who had shared his life and his bed ...
Susy whom he openly admitted he desired ...

'I ...'

'Your body wants me,' Jake told her thickly,
the sound of his voice muffled as his mouth
explored the soft skin just below the neckline of
her lace top. Fireworks exploded inside her,
making her arch instinctively, her breasts lifting
and swelling in open desire. The delicate touch of
Jake's fingers as he gradually drew away the
neckline of her underwear was almost more than
she could stand. When his lips finally began to
explore the smooth slope of her breasts she
tensed in expectation, desire twisting and coiling
through her stomach.

'You want me, admit it.' His tongue traced a
circle round her nipple, making her ache with the
intensity of her need. Her fingers slid into his
hair, her body arching hungrily against his
mouth. 'Tell me you want me ...'

'I want you ...' the admission burst past her
lips, followed by a wave of fear so great that she
added feverishly, 'I want you, Jake and I don't
deny it, but it's only physical desire, I ... don't
feel anything else for you.'

'Only physical desire,' his voice was suddenly
ice-cold and, to Stephanie's shock, he suddenly
thrust her away, sitting up and running his
fingers through his hair. In the half light it was
impossible for her to see the expression in his
eyes, and despite the warmth of the fire, she
shivered. 'It seems to me that I've made a
miscalculation somewhere.'

'What did you want me to say?' Stephanie demanded tautly, not knowing why she had to torment herself by saying the words, but saying them nevertheless, 'That I love you?'

'Well, my ego would certainly have appreciated hearing that after waiting two years to get you into my arms.'

'I don't believe you've wanted me for all that time,' Stephanie threw at him, quivering with rejection and loss. 'You're just using me as a substitute for Susy, and because ... because ... like all men you can't bear to think that there's a woman who's immune to you.'

In the dense silence that followed, Stephanie felt she could almost hear the foundations of their friendship cracking, and it gave her no consolation to know she had contributed to its destruction.

Without answering her Jake started to fasten his shirt. 'Look, let's forget this whole thing happened.' His voice was totally without expression.

'How can we forget it? Jake, I can't work for you any longer. You must see that ...'

'You can't leave without giving me three months' written notice—it's in your contract—remember?'

Stephanie gasped in pain. 'But you wouldn't hold me to that ... you ...'

'You seem to be having trouble deciding just what our roles in connection with one another are, right now,' he countered acidly. 'You can't have it all ways, Stephanie. Make up your mind whether you want us to be friends, lovers, or simply employer and employee, and when you have, you can let me know. But remember this, I won't let you just walk out on me—right now I'm in the middle of some very delicate negotiations in Florida—we're due to fly out there next month, and if you decide to leave, I'll make you serve every day of those three months.'

'But, how can we work together now?' Stephanie asked him wildly. 'We can't simply pretend . . .'

'You mean you can't,' Jake responded bitterly. 'Haven't you listened to a single thing I said? I've been doing it for the last two years. It isn't so hard once you get the hang of it . . . and perhaps it's time you learned that life isn't always easy. You know, I was wrong about one thing,' he added decisively, glancing at the silk satin that covered her body so enticingly, 'I thought that wearing it might turn you into a woman. All it did was reinforce how wrong I was. You're a coward, Stephanie. You're afraid to admit that you want me and to take the consequences of that wanting. Oh, I know exactly why you told me it was only "physical desire",' he told her bitterly, 'But if you ever change your mind, you're going to have to tell me about it. I'm tired of making the decisions for you and taking the blame.'

'I'm going to bed,' Stephanie told him unsteadily. 'Good night, Jake.'

She edged past him, not daring to look at him, frightened of the anger she seemed to have aroused in him, but surely *she* should be the one to feel angry? She was the one who was the injured party. Jake seemed to care nothing for the fact that their friendship was over . . . but then, by his own admission, on his side it had never really existed.

Biting hard on her lip to prevent herself from crying, Stephanie hurried out of the room. So much had happened tonight that she could barely take it all in. Only one thing was clear . . . even if he could force her to work her three months' notice, Jake couldn't stop her leaving ultimately, and as for going to him and telling him she wanted him . . . She shuddered as she pulled off her suit, almost tearing the camiknickers in her urgency to blot out the memory of Jake's taunting words, flinging them on to the floor as she groped for her cotton nightdress. At least Jake's room was far enough away from hers for him not to hear if she gave way now to the tears that had been threatening during their final moments together. She couldn't even take comfort from the fact that he desired her. Not when she knew that desire was only because she was there and Susy was not.

CHAPTER SEVEN

TRYING to treat Jake as merely her boss was something Stephanie found increasingly difficult once they had returned to London. If he *had* desired her, she couldn't understand how he had managed to keep it hidden from her. Where once she had looked at him and simply seen a man who was her closest friend, now she couldn't even glance at him without being acutely aware that he was the man she loved. Just the sound of his voice was enough to make her weak with longing, and although she was determined not to let her efficiency suffer, she wondered if Jake was aware of how deeply her feelings had changed. The temptation to reach out and touch him, to beg him to make love to her was so strong at times that she feared it would overwhelm her, but what was the use? He didn't love her!

Another thing she had noticed since her return to London was a certain cooling in Jessie's manner. At first she had been confused and then later hurt by her new friend's defection, although it wasn't until Jessie asked, almost curtly, on the Friday after her return, 'Did you enjoy your weekend?' that she began to guess the reason for her changed attitude.

'It was . . .' On the point of fibbing that her weekend had been enjoyable, she changed her mind and admitted bleakly. 'Jessica, I should have told you. I didn't spend the weekend with friends—I was down at Mile End, Jake's home. We were working, but after what you said about the gossip, I panicked and I'm afraid I lied to you.'

'Yes, I know.' The expression in Jessie's eyes softened a little. 'You were seen by one of the other girls getting out of Jake's car on Monday evening. I'm afraid it's all round the office. I was asked if I knew anything about it.'

'What did you say?'

'Nothing,' Jessie assured her, 'and I'm sorry if I've been a bit prickly this week, but . . .'

'I can understand why you were annoyed,' Stephanie told her quietly, 'but the gossip should die down once I leave.'

'Leave? You're leaving?'

'I've had to give Jake three months' notice. But, yes, I will be leaving once I've worked it.'

'But Stephanie, why? The pair of you make such a good team . . . Like Batman and Robin.'

Stephanie laughed as she had intended her to. 'Unfortunately—unlike Batman and Robin—our relationship is subject to certain complications . . .'

'Now that means one of two things,' Jessie interrupted shrewdly, 'either you've fallen madly in love with him, or he's made a pass at you.' She saw Stephanie's expression and whistled soundlessly. 'Ah, I think I've got it, right on both counts is that it?'

Grimacing faintly, Stephanie nodded. 'I suppose it was bound to happen,' Jessie consoled her. 'I don't know how you've managed to work with him for so long without succumbing, and, as for Jake ... well, he wouldn't be male if he wasn't aware of you. I can understand why you want to leave. It must be pure hell, loving him and yet knowing he just fancies you.'

'Umm ... As yet, he hasn't guessed how I feel, and I don't want him to.'

'No, I can understand that, but it's odd,' Jessie frowned. 'I mean, a man like him, he's just got to know the signs. I'll bet girls have been running after him ever since he started wearing long trousers, and normally, when a man wants a little dalliance, he runs a mile the moment he senses the girl's getting serious. You don't suppose he feels more strongly about you than he's letting on?'

'When he's conducting a full-blooded affair with Susy Waldron?'

'No ... I suppose you're right. Look, how about spending Saturday evening at our place?' Jessie suggested. 'Keith will be there.'

'Thanks, Jessie, but I really don't feel it's fair of me to inflict my company on anyone right at the moment. Perhaps another time?'

In point of fact, she was far too tired to be good company in any case. Ever since she had handed Jake her typewritten notice immediately following their return to London, he had treated her with a chill civility that made a mockery of all her trust in their friendship and that, coupled with the gruelling pace of work he was setting, combined to make her too exhausted to do anything other than simply flop down in a chair when she got home in the evening.

Annette commented on it. Back from her holiday with her fiancé, she surveyed Stephanie's wan face with concern.

'He always did make you work hard, but can't he see you're wasting away in front of him?' she demanded, when Stephanie pushed away her meal, barely tasted. 'What's wrong with you? You won't eat, you don't sleep properly ... Honestly, Stephanie, anyone would think you're in love.'

Stephanie hadn't told her that she had handed in her notice. She hadn't made any plans for the future and had not even started to look for another job. She seemed to be in some sort of limbo, held there by the fear that any attempts to break free of it would result in a pain too terrible to endure.

One day followed another, with Jake steadily growing more remote and cold, and Stephanie felt as though she were dying by degrees. In some ways, she welcomed his withdrawal from her; it made it easier to endure the pain of loving him, knowing her love wasn't returned. At least, that was what she told herself until the afternoon she returned from lunch and found Susy in Jake's arms.

She had walked into his office without a second thought, believing him to be still at lunch. He had told her he had a lunch engagement and, believing that Susy was still in New York, she had never dreamed who his engagement might be with. The sight of the pair of them locked together, unaware of her interruption, brought a sudden spasm of sickness too acute to be ignored.

Backing out of the room, Stephanie raced into the cloakroom, gagging helplessly beneath the onslaught of nausea. 'You're sick with jealousy.' Jake's words came back to her and she shivered under the acknowledgement that he had been right. Night after night, she dared not go to sleep because her dreams tormented her with images of him with Susy and now those nightmares had turned into reality. Rinsing her mouth, she walked slowly back to her office, this time making a considerable amount of noise as she opened the door.

'Ah, there you are,' Jake came out of his office. His dark hair was ruffled, and Stephanie could see that the top buttons of his shirt were unfastened, his tie faintly askew. Nausea churned up inside her again.

He gave her a sharp look. 'You look pale. Are you feeling all right?'

'Just a headache,' she lied, avoiding his eyes.

'I'm just taking Susy to see one of the new apartments we've taken on. I don't know what time we'll be back.'

As he spoke, Susy walked out of his office. Her make-up had been carefully touched up, but nothing could disguise the soft swelling of her lips or the look in her eyes.

'Darling, if I have anything to do with you, you won't be coming back,' she purred softly. 'Why don't you change your mind and come back to New York with me, next week? Take a break . . .'

'I only wish I could, but we're so busy at the moment . . .'

Stephanie tensed, waiting for him to tell the other woman that he would be in the States later in the month, but, to her surprise, he said nothing. Perhaps he wanted to save it for a surprise, she thought acidly as they walked out. Jealousy, corrosive and full-blown, ripped apart all her dearly held convictions that civilised, thinking adults just did not give in to such destructive emotions. For a moment, seeing Susy's polished fingernails resting on Jake's dark-suited arm, she had wanted to annihilate her.

She spent almost the entire weekend thinking about them, imagining them together. Susy would have no inhibitions about showing Jake just how much she wanted him. She would not care that he didn't love her. Cold fingers of anguish touched Stephanie's heart. What if Jake *did* love her? Could he love someone as shallow as Susy? Once she would have said 'no', but now she was beginning to wonder if she had ever really known Jake, if all that she had known of him was simply what he had deliberately allowed her to know. In many ways, she wished she could go back to that time when she hadn't known what sexual desire and jealousy were, where she had been content and secure, but somehow her emotional responses had been reactivated as suddenly as they had been blighted and her body was a feverish, restless ache that gave her no rest from torment.

The following week, Jake told her to make their travel arrangements.

To her enquiry as to how long they would be away, he retorted with a curt, 'Does it matter?' Across the width of his desk, his eyes probed hers, and Stephanie tensed, terrified by what they might discover.

'I do have friends and social engagements to consider,' she managed in cool response.

'Friends?' Again, his steel-grey glance meshed with hers. 'Do you mean the guy I saw kissing you outside your flat?'

'Keith is one of my friends, yes,' Stephanie agreed bravely.

'Keith?' Jake came round from behind his desk and strode towards her. He reminded her of an angry leopard, Stephanie thought in panic. She could almost feel the tension emanating from his body, and she was chilled by the ferocity of the look he gave her.

'And does this "friend" know exactly what friendship with you means, Stephanie? Does he know that he'll be allowed to go so far, and no further ... or is he still living in hopes that he might actually get to go to bed with you?'

Her breath was caught in a pained gasp that fluttered and died in her throat.

'Perhaps he's already taken you to bed,' Jake suggested, apparently oblivious to her anguish, his eyes glittering febrilely as he loomed over her. 'Has he, Stephanie? Has he?' He was actually grasping her arms and shaking her, rage and hostility openly apparent in his eyes. 'Or are you planning to torment him the way you tormented me ...'

'I didn't ...' Somehow she managed to stammer the denial, 'I didn't do anything ...'

'No, you damn well didn't, did you?' Jake agreed, almost snarling the words. 'God, you've got me so I can't even think straight. Have you any idea what you're doing to me ...?'

'If you're suffering from frustration, I suggest you blame Susy, not me,' Stephanie hurled back at him, now nearly as angry as he was himself, stunned when he suddenly went pale and lurched against his desk, releasing her to grip it with fingers white to the bone.

'Jake . . .' she reached out automatically concerned for him, but he brushed away her hand, exhibiting an anger and rejection that couldn't be ignored. 'Jake . . . what is it? What's wrong?'

'Don't ask,' he responded bitterly in a voice she barely recognised. For a moment, he sounded like an old man, weary beyond belief, beaten down by life. 'Don't ask, Stephanie,' he repeated harshly. 'You're really better off not knowing . . . and anyway, you damned well don't want to know.' Just for a moment, as he looked at her, his eyes seemed to hold the torment of someone experiencing an unendurable pain, and then he turned his head and the look was gone.

'Do you know something, Stephanie,' he said savagely, 'I feel heart-sorry for the poor devil who eventually makes you accept that you're a woman, because you'll put him through hell first. Now get out . . .'

'But the flight arrangements?'

'I'll make them myself. Right now, I want you out of this office, Stephanie. I don't care where you go or what you do . . . just go . . .'

She had gone then, back to her flat to cry herself into exhaustion, totally bewildered by their quarrel, not knowing why he had been so angry, or why he had reacted so violently to her suggestion that his frustration should be laid at Susy's door.

In the morning, he was as cold and remote as she had grown used to him being, dealing with their heavy work load with a speed that made her wonder savagely if he was human. By lunch time, he had given her enough work to keep her occupied until well after six.

He had appointments in the afternoon, and it was gone five when he eventually came back. All the urgent mail was done, but Stephanie was determined not to leave until she had finished, and it was this that kept her doggedly typing on when her fingers already ached to the bone with tiredness.

'Not finished?' His sarcastic comment made her seethe with anger, but she refused to give way to it.

'How long are you going to be?'

She glanced at her notebook, flipping through the still untyped pages. 'About an hour—maybe an hour and a half.'

She heard him go into his office and recognised the squeaking protest of his chair as he sat down. The intense silence that followed was unnerving and, although she tried to concentrate on her work, her mind kept wandering. Why didn't he just sign his mail and go, her mind screamed protestingly. She *couldn't* work while he was sitting in there. Her fingers stumbled over the keys.

'Something wrong?' He came to stand in the doorway between their offices, leaning indolently there, whilst he studied her flushed face. He had removed his jacket and rolled up his sleeves, the dark hairs on his arms bringing back vibrantly real memories of the crispness of his body hair beneath her fingers. The ability to breathe normally suddenly left her, her heart labouring under the strain his proximity imposed upon it.

'Please stop watching me, it makes me nervous.' The admission was out before she could stop it. 'Jake, why don't you go home?' she added nervously, 'I can't work with you prowling about like . . . like a restless panther . . .'

'Panther? Is that how you see me?' One eyebrow rose mockingly. 'Would you like to know how I see you?'

'No, I'd like you to leave me in peace so that I can get on with my work and go home,' Stephanie said shortly.

'Umm, clock-watching now, are we? Why? Got a heavy date tonight?' The mockery in his voice stung as though he knew quite well that there were no other men in her life and why.

'It isn't any of your business if I have,' she retorted angrily. 'Have you signed your mail?'

'No, but I will.' He moved away from the wall and strolled back into his own room. Trying to compose herself Stephanie tried to concentrate on her work. By the time she had typed another full page she knew it was a losing battle. Even without reading what she had done she could see half a-dozen mistakes. Her ears were stretched for the slightest indication of movement from the other room, and yet, when it came, Jake caught her off-guard. Her ribbon cartridge ran out right in the middle of a line and she got up to get another one. She was kneeling down with her back to the door, as she looked in the cupboard for a fresh one, when she suddenly knew that Jake was in the room with her. Whirling round, she was stunned to discover that he was standing by her typewriter studying what she had just done.

'Staying any longer seems to be a complete waste of time if that's the best you can do,' he announced laconically, ripping the sheet of paper out of the machine. 'Get your coat. I'll take you home.'

Her chin tilting dangerously, Stephanie said. 'There's no need. I can take the bus . . .'

'Oh yes . . . and we both know what happened the last time you did that, don't we? What's the matter, Stephanie? Has your new boyfriend given you so much courage that you aren't afraid any more? If he has, he's achieved a damned sight more than I was ever able to do, hasn't he?' he ended savagely. 'No more arguments. I'm taking you home.'

Following him down to his car, Stephanie tried to relax, knowing it was impossible. Inside his car, the familiar scents of leather and Jake's cologne enveloped her. She leaned back in her seat, closing her eyes. Perhaps, if she couldn't see him, she wouldn't be so powerfully affected by his presence. Her eyes flew open as she felt his breath brush her face, her startled gaze meeting his tight one.

'You forgot this,' he told her, handing her the seat belt, 'or had you forgotten it's become law now?'

Feeling like a fool, she fastened it quickly, hoping that Jake wouldn't notice the dull flush of colour staining her skin. Normally, a good driver with whom she felt completely relaxed, tonight for some reason there was an unleased impatience about the way he handled the car, and she felt as though there were nothing he would like better than to give it its head.

'Don't look so worried,' he drawled, mis-interpreting the look she gave him. 'I'm not about to carry you off to my bed.' He turned away from her, and muttered something Stephanie couldn't quite catch but that sounded like 'much good it would do either of us,' and she flushed again at the implication behind the words. Did he honestly believe she wasn't woman enough to respond to his caresses and to give him the pleasure he was no doubt accustomed to sharing with women like Susy? Perhaps she wasn't ... perhaps love was not an adequate substitute for experience. Stephanie closed her eyes, knowing that if she didn't she wouldn't be able to stop herself from reaching out to touch him; from giving in to the fierce hunger that grew daily inside her.

'You're home, Stephanie.' The dry words brought her back to reality with a start. She hadn't even realised that Jake had stopped the car.

'Did you manage to make all the arrangements for Florida?' It was the first thing that came into her head, and his mouth tightened slightly as he listened to her.

'I managed,' he told her curtly. We leave at eight-thirty on Monday morning. You'd better spend Sunday evening at my place. We'll go by taxi from there. There's no need to look at me like that,' he told her. 'I've already said it once. If you want me to repeat it I will. The only way you're going to get into my bed, Stephanie, is by begging me to take you there, which leaves your virtue pretty steel-clad, wouldn't you say?'

He drove off before she could retort, and it was only as she inserted her key in her lock that Stephanie realised that it was the first time he had ever brought her home at night and not seen her safely inside her flat, and somehow that made her want to cry more than all that had gone before.

CHAPTER EIGHT

'COMFORTABLE?'

Stephanie nodded her head as she fastened her seat belt for the long flight to Florida. After all her dread about staying at Jake's apartment overnight, the evening had passed without incident. Jake had shut himself in his study almost from the moment they arrived at his apartment, and hadn't emerged at eleven o'clock when Stephanie had decided to go to bed. She had lain there sleepless, listening to the alien night sounds around her, shivering slightly as she recalled his low-voiced comment to her that if she wanted to share his bed she would have to beg for permission to do so.

Knowing that the flight would be a long one, Stephanie had brought with her a thick paperback epic she had been promising herself she would read for months, and in the airport Jake had bought her a large pile of glossy magazines. As soon as the take-off procedure was completed, and they were free to unfasten their seat belts, Jake opened his briefcase, and started work. Stephanie who had flown with him before had known what to expect, but on this occasion she felt a tiny flare of pain that he could block out her presence so easily, when she had to fight constantly against her awareness of him.

Within an hour of take-off, the stewardesses

were serving breakfast. Stephanie accepted only
fruit juice and coffee, noticing that Jake did the
same. Afterwards, he turned back to his work,
leaving her to stare aimlessly through the
window.

'Bored?'

She hadn't realised he was watching her. 'No
. . . my book . . .'

'Doesn't seem to be holding your attention.
I've got some contracts to check, would you do it
with me?'

Nodding her agreement, Stephanie took the
sheaf of papers he held out, trying not to
remember all those occasions in the past when
they had worked together in amicable harmony
Now, all that was gone. Suppressing a sigh, she
tried to concentrate on the typed pages she was
holding. The purpose of their visit to Florida was
so that Jake could formally complete a partnership
deal he was entering with an American real estate
company, to sell and rent condo apartments and
villas for holiday and retirement purposes.

The negotiations had been protracted and
slow-moving. Jake was anxious to protect the
interests of potential buyers and had required
certain guarantees and sub-clauses to be inserted
in the contract, which had delayed its completion.
Now the contract was ready for signature, and the
first villas and condo block built by the American
company were finished. The plan was for a small,
self-contained complex to be built along the
coast, complete with swimming pools, a small
shopping centre and library, and of course the
mandatory American sports complex. Because the

part of Florida Keys where the construction was taking place was remote, Jake had been concerned for its desirability for those people who might buy the villas as potential holiday homes, and this had involved the construction of a new road to link up with the main highway.

'You managed to get them to agree to free membership for the golf club, then?' Stephanie commented, so immersed in the contract that, for a moment, she forgot the atmosphere between them.

Jake, too, seemed willing to overlook it as he explained.

'Yes, for many of the older people, living on a fixed income, the golf course is more important than the sports complex, and the fact that they might have to pay inflated fees to join could put them off buying. I've deliberately delayed this visit because I wanted to see for myself just what standard the dwellings have been finished to. That's why I've arranged for us to stay in one of the villas,' he added calmly.

'We're staying in one of the villas?' Stephanie couldn't prevent the panic from creeping up into her voice. 'But I thought you'd booked us into one of the hotels in Miami.'

'It wouldn't have been practical. We'd have had to travel out to the site almost every day to check on progress. I decided we could judge the site far better if we actually stayed there. The sports complex is finished, and so is the larger swimming pool. I intend to test them all out. The shopping arcade isn't finished yet, and as we'll have to be self-sufficient, I've arranged a hire car so that you can go into town to pick up whatever

supplies we need. It's the best way of testing the
viability of the site. I've also set up a meeting
with Brice Challoner who's going to handle the
PR side of things and act generally as our
representative at the Florida end.

'Brice Challoner?'

'He's a partner in Challoner and Hearst, the
real estate agents we've dealt with before in
Florida, and he also has connections with Hearst
Meadows, the PR company we're using.'

'Yes, of course, I recognise his name,'
Stephanie murmured, turning her attention back
to the contract, a cold shaft of fear touching her
heart. Once Jake would have discussed all these
arrangements with her before making them . . .
but, of course, now that she had handed in her
notice . . . Blinking away betraying tears she tried
to concentrate.

They were served lunch, which Stephanie
barely touched; watched a film, and were served
another meal, and then, just as Stephanie began
to feel tiredness claiming her, they began to
descend.

Even travelling first class, there was the
inevitable hassle collecting their luggage and, by
the time they eventually left the airport building,
she was feeling totally disorientated, both by the
long flight and the time change, so much so, that
she almost lost Jake when he abruptly veered off,
heading for a man standing searching the crowd,
his deep tan and wheat-blond hair making him
distinctive even amongst the bronzed crowds of
holidaymakers in the airport terminal.

'Hi, you must be Jake,' he announced breezily,

shaking Jake's hand, his eyes riveted on Stephanie, 'and this?'

'My secretary, Stephanie Walters,' Jake introduced curtly. 'Thanks for meeting us.'

'No problem. Hi, Stephanie. I'm Brice Challoner.'

'Nice to meet you Mr Challoner,' Stephanie returned formally, holding out her hand. It was almost lost in the tanned breadth of his, blue eyes twinkling as he grinned down at her.

'No "Misters" here, honey ... we don't go in for that sort of thing, and besides, I hate to hear a beautiful girl, calling me "Mister"; it kinda makes me feel old.'

He was somewhere about Jake's age, in his early thirties, Stephanie guessed, but with a breezy, good-natured manner that made him seem younger.

'The car's out back. I've hired one for you and it's down at the complex. Anything you want whilst you're here, just give me a call. Right now, I expect you folks are feeling pretty tired. We've got a fair drive ahead of us, but the traffic shouldn't be so bad.'

'How will people arriving to spend holidays in the villas get there?' Stephanie asked, thinking of their long flight and the inevitable muzziness and exhaustion at the end of it. A long drive to their final destination would be daunting to parents arriving with small families, and might put them off using the villas.

'Good point,' Jake broke in.

'Well, most of them will probably organise hire cars, but we can work something out. Arrange a welcoming service, if you like. It shouldn't be too difficult.' He grinned at Stephanie. 'Beautiful and efficient. Now that's a combination I like. If you ever decide you'd like to work in the States, I could use a good secretary, especially one with an accent like yours. English secretaries are something of a status symbol around here.'

Was he serious, Stephanie wondered with a thudding heart? If so, his offer might be the ideal solution to her dilemma. Even if she could find another job as good as the one she had with Jake in London, living there would be a constant torment and reminder of what she had lost. She had good qualifications and, although working abroad had never particularly appealed to her, there might be something to be said for putting the width of the Atlantic Ocean between them. She glanced up at Jake, almost automatically, and wished she hadn't when she saw the grim look tensing his mouth.

'If you're thinking what I think you're thinking,' he gritted at her as Brice walked ahead to unlock the doors of a gleaming Mercedes, 'then don't. For one thing, I wouldn't give you a good enough reference.'

'Perhaps he'll take me without,' Stephanie replied flippantly '. . . on the strength of his own judgement.'

'Right now, the only level his judgement's working on is how good you'd be in bed,' Jake told her brutally.

Their proximity to Brice's car prevented Stephanie from making any further response. She was careful to take the back seat of the car, leaving the front free for Jake but, to her surprise, he elected to slide in beside her, his thigh brushing against hers as he subsided into the seat.

'You gave us all a surprise when you said you'd stay at the villa,' Brice remarked, as they drew out of the parking lot. 'We thought you'd stay in Miami.'

'If I'm going to recommend and sell the complex to my clients, I want to be sure of what they're getting,' Jake responded briskly. 'American and British ideas as to what takes priority sometimes differ.'

'Yeah, well, of course, you know that the maid service isn't functional yet—only half a dozen or so villas have been completed. We've put you in a two-bedroomed one.' In the driving mirror, Stephanie saw his eyes meet Jake's in silent query, and her cheeks burned at the implications in the look they exchanged.

'That's fine,' Jake responded easily. 'Am I right in thinking that the villas so far completed form a semi-village concept around their own pool?'

'That's right. All these villas are of the smaller design—the larger ones have their own pools. We thought they would be suitable for retired couples. They've been designed for easy running, and they're all within easy reach of all the facilities.'

As the two men continued to chat, Stephanie wondered why Jake hadn't taken the front passenger seat. Her eyelids felt heavy and she was longing to sleep. Reluctantly she let them close. Perhaps, if she just rested them for a few minutes . . .

'Stephanie . . .'

Reluctantly, she forced her eyes open. They felt as though iron weights were attached to their lids. She felt warm and comfortable, protected in a way she hadn't felt, oh . . . for longer than she could remember. Beneath her cheek was something warm and reassuringly solid. Something firm held her round her waist, and she didn't really want to move.

'Stephanie, wake up. We're here.'

Jake! She was with Jake! As she struggled into a sitting position, Stephanie realised that she had been sleeping in his arms with her head on his shoulder. Trying to appear calm and unflustered, she glanced in the driving mirror. Brice Challoner was watching her speculatively.

'I'm sorry I fell asleep on you, like that,' she apologised to Jake. 'The long flight . . .'

Jake flexed his arm, and grimaced faintly, as though it were numb, as Brice turned off the main road and the car bumped over an unmade-up track that seemed to meander without purpose through the chaos of the construction site.

'You aren't seeing it at its best,' he warned them. 'You'll have to exercise your imagination to see all this lot lawned and planted with trees. You've seen the site plans?'

This last question was addressed to Jake, who nodded his head.

'I guess when I drop you off, you'll both want to catch up on your sleep. How about if I give you a call tomorrow morning?'

'Fine,' Jake agreed, as the car turned the corner, and Stephanie saw the villas in front of them.

Built in a Mexican-cum-Spanish style, they presented curiously blank fronts, which Brice explained would eventually be softened by climbing plants. 'The architects' idea was to create a sort of enclosed, almost Moorish effect, which you can judge best from inside. All the villas have their own backyards and keys that let them into the completely private pool area beyond. It's quite effective, but I won't come in with you now. I'll leave you to explore for yourselves.' He had stopped the car and turned to smile at Stephanie.

'Sorry about falling asleep like that,' she apologised, flushing slightly beneath his wryly amused regard.

'Think nothing of it, honey,' he told her. 'I only wish a beautiful girl like you would turn into my arms like a homing pigeon coming to roost. No wonder you chose to sit in the back seat, Jake,' he chuckled.

He was only teasing them, Stephanie knew, and there was as little reason for her to feel so acutely embarrassed as there was for the look of intense anger that glittered briefly in Jake's eyes.

'Car's in the garage. Here are the keys.' Brice tossed a bunch of keys to Jake. 'See you folks tomorrow.'

Jake lifted their cases out of the car's deep trunk and then Brice reversed away, leaving them alone.

'Shall we go in?'

The small close had a raw, unfinished air to it, and Stephanie shivered slightly. 'They had to get the villa furnished for us to occupy it, so Heaven knows what it will be like,' Jake told her, putting the key in the door, 'but if American efficiency is all it's supposed to be, we should find it quite liveable in.'

Following him inside, Stephanie stared around with appreciation. They were in a large living-room-cum-hall, with the stairs rising out of it. At the opposite end of the room, patio windows opened out on to what Brice had described as the 'yard' but what was, in effect, a very attractive and good-sized garden.

'Kitchen and dining room should be through there,' Jake said, indicating two doors. 'Do you want to go and investigate while I take our cases up? I wouldn't mind a cup of coffee if you could rustle one up . . .'

The kitchen seemed to possess every electrical gadget known, plus an enticing selection of fresh and frozen food.

'There's enough stuff here to feed an army,' Stephanie couldn't resist muttering to herself as she found a percolator and opened a can of coffee. Jake preferred his made from fresh beans, and she made a mental note to buy some if she got the chance.

'How is it?'

She hadn't heard him come downstairs and tensed, glancing hesitantly towards him.

'Everything's fine. The kitchen seems to be a housewife's paradise.'

'Or a househusband's,' Jake drawled. 'Don't forget you're in the States now, where they take sexual equality very seriously. Coffee ready?'

'Your chauvinism is showing,' Stephanie teased him, pouring him a cup, forgetting for a moment the gulf that now lay between them. 'I'll try and get some fresh beans tomorrow,' she added grinning at his wry expression as he took a sip. 'How does the villa measure up so far?'

'On the face of it, quite well. Both bedrooms are a good size, and both have fully equipped bathrooms. I'm going to take a look outside. Why don't you try and catch up on your sleep?'

Hurt that he didn't invite her to accompany him, Stephanie busied herself pouring herself a cup of coffee.

'Will we be eating in?'

'I think so. With the flight and the time difference, we're both totally disorientated. No doubt Brice will want to take us out to dinner tomorrow. You definitely made a hit there, but don't get too excited about that job offer he made you. Something tells me that sharing an office wasn't all he had in mind, and we both know how you'd feel about sharing his bed.'

'Do we?' Suddenly, Stephanie was angry. 'What makes you think that, Jake? For all you know, I could be quite happy about the prospect. After all, he's an extremely attractive man.' She brushed past him before he could say anything. Let him go and explore their surroundings on his own if that's what he wanted!

She heard the hired car drive away as she undressed. Her bedroom had a small balcony, complete with a table and two chairs, and it overlooked both the garden and the pool area beyond. A castellated wall surrounded the pool area which had been planted with irregular islands of spreading plants, the walls already showing faint hints of green where the climbing roses and bougainvillaea would eventually spread. The pool itself was large and well-designed, with plenty of room for sitting out and a raised barbecue area at one end. Sighing, Stephanie wandered into her bathroom. As Jake had said, it was impressively luxurious. The water ran hot and smooth, filling the small sunken tub. She sank down into the milky water, letting her muscles relax. She was almost half asleep when she realised the water was getting cold. Too tired even to think of preparing a meal, she got out, wrapping herself in a towel, and went to lie down on her bed, letting her eyes close.

'Stephanie?'

She came to with a start. She had slept so deeply that she hadn't even moved. Her skin felt quite cool beneath the damp towel she was still wearing, and she shrugged it off automatically.

'Stephanie, are you all right?' The bedroom door opened and Jake strode in, stopping abruptly when he saw her. She paused in the act of sitting up, her face flaming when she realised that Jake was there.

'I fell asleep. You woke me.' Clumsily she reached for the towel, forgetting that she was still half-lying on it, the cool wind from the open balcony window raising goosebumps of flesh on her skin. She hadn't even unpacked, she remembered, and the clothes she had arrived in were still lying on the bathroom floor.

'For God's sake, get some clothes on.' Jake's harsh demand ignited her temper.

'There's nothing I'd like more,' she told him acidly, 'but my suitcase is over there,' she pointed towards the opposite side of the room, 'and the clothes I travelled in are in the bathroom.'

'Do you make a habit of lying around naked?' The insolent glance skimming her body that accompanied his taunting drawl inflamed her temper further.

'Do you make a habit of walking into people's bedrooms uninvited? I'm sorry if you find the sight of my ... of my body offensive,' her chin jutted out stubbornly, 'but I didn't invite you to walk in here.'

'Offensive?' For a moment, he almost sounded startled, and then a derisory gleam entered his eyes. 'Whatever gave you that idea?' he asked softly, closing the door and coming towards her. Outside, night had fallen and the air was full of strange sounds. Tensing, Stephanie watched his approach with eyes unknowingly dark in the pale oval of her face.

'Aggravating ... enticing ... arousing, yes, but offensive?' He shook his head, his mouth curling faintly as he witnessed her tension. 'Tell me, Stephanie, why is it that Brice Challoner can flirt with you with impunity, while 1 only have to look at you to have you scuttling behind that protective wall you're so fond of?'

'You ... you're different.'

'Different?' He was so close to her now that Stephanie could see his chest rising and falling as he breathed. Did he have the slightest idea of the effect he had on her? This close to him, it was almost impossible to think rationally.

'How am I different? Different because I know the truth about you? Because . . .'

As Stephanie turned away from him, wanting to hide from the harsh sound of his voice, her body was silhouetted for a brief instant by the moonlight pouring in through the uncurtained window. She heard Jake catch his breath, and realised that he had gone as tense as a predator about to pounce.

'For Christ's sake, Stephanie, get some clothes on,' he grated thickly, 'otherwise, I . . .'

'You'll what?' Stephanie taunted bitterly. 'Forget that you said I'd have to beg to get into your bed, and that I'm not Susy . . . Does she know how frustration affects you? That you turn to any woman who happens to be handy when she's not there . . .?'

'Is that what you think?' So suddenly that she didn't have the opportunity to escape, his fingers clamped round her wrist, pulling her upright into a sitting position. Acutely conscious of her nudity, Stephanie cowered away.

'You're very fond of accusing me of using you as a substitute for Susy aren't you?' he muttered harshly. 'Well, this should give you a laugh. I've never touched her in the way that you mean Stephanie. Oh, I wanted to . . .' he gritted when he saw her disbelieving expression. 'God, you can't know how I've wanted to.' Pain bit deeply into her at his admission. Was he saying that he loved Susy? 'But I couldn't,' he continued, 'I haven't touched any other women in the two years I've known you. That's the effect you've had on me. You've practically destroyed me as a man, turned me into a eunuch who can't function properly.' His fingers bit more deeply into her wrist. 'I've wanted you . . . ached for you until I've nearly gone crazy with it, knowing that you didn't want me. Whilst you didn't want any other man either it was bearable—just about. I tried dating other women, but all I could see when I touched them was your face . . . your eyes, looking at me the way they looked the night you were attacked.'

'Jake . . .'

'Don't start . . .' he warned her. 'I'm not in the mood for it Stephanie. The only thing that's kept me going all this time is the gut feeling that, one day, you'd wake up from your nightmare and that we'd pick up where we left off before you were attacked. The *only* thing,' he reiterated, 'but you just don't want to know, do you? You're just too damn happy in that private little world you've built for yourself to even think of coming out.'

'Jake . . . I never knew . . .'

'Because I took damn good care not to let you. You'd have run a mile if you'd known that I wanted you physically. You've become an obsession with me, Stephanie; an obstacle I can't get round, or under, and until I do I'm useless as a man. If you don't believe me, ask Susy. I think she's beginning to get suspicious about the number of headaches I get,' he added sardonically, releasing her. 'Now perhaps you understand why coming in here and finding you naked doesn't exactly help.'

'I didn't ask you to come in, or to . . . want me . . .'

'Stephanie, you ask me every time you look at me,' he told her harshly. 'You may not know it, but you do. You want me all right, but you're too damned scared to admit it . . . God, do you think I want to feel like this about you? Do you think I really wouldn't prefer to be able to . . . Oh God, what's the use?' he said tiredly. 'You don't even begin to understand . . . I'm not sure I do myself. Do you want to eat?'

When she shook her head, he turned back towards the door. 'I've got some work to do. I'll see you in the morning.'

After he had gone, Stephanie curled up into a small ball on the bed, her mind trying to grasp what he had told her. An obsession, Jake had told her, and that admission had been dragged from the very depths of his soul. She had turned him into a eunuch he had said . . . She shivered, sitting up. Dear God . . . she had never known . . . never guessed that what had happened to her might have had an equally traumatic effect on him. He had wanted her before she was attacked he had said, intimating that, but for that, they would have been lovers. She got off the bed, and went to her suitcase, opening it and searching automatically for her robe. Jake! Her heart ached with love and pity for him. She had just seen him stripped of pride, admitting something to her no man ever wanted to admit. But what could she do?

Slowly, pulling on her robe, she sat back and thought, and then she knew.

CHAPTER NINE

HER heart thumping, Stephanie glanced at her watch. Two o'clock. Surely Jake would be asleep now? She had heard him come to bed over an hour ago. She listened and, hearing no sounds from the adjacent room, slid stealthily out of bed. What she was about to do called for a degree of courage and nerve control she wasn't sure she had, but . . .

No second thoughts now, she told herself firmly, opening her bedroom door and letting her breath out in a faint exhalation of relief when she saw no light showing under Jake's door. She had been frightened that he might have taken some work to bed with him.

The door wasn't closed, and she pushed it open, praying it wouldn't squeak. It didn't. The room was an exact replica of her own. In the moonlight, she could make out Jake's tousled dark head and lean form. He lay quite still, one arm flung out across the bedclothes. Nervous dread coiled in the pit of her stomach. Dear God, had she gone mad? She couldn't go through with this . . . She could not walk over to that bed and calmly start making love to Jake, no matter how much she owed him.

She could, and she would, even if it meant she was freeing him to go to Susy. Her mouth twisted drily. Did the other woman know why Jake hadn't yet been her lover, or did she simply think he was playing hard to get? It was a novel thought and one that made her mouth twitch with appreciation. Hysteria, she warned herself firmly. There was nothing remotely amusing about what had happened to them. She was in love with a man who didn't love her, but who did desire her—to the extent where his need to consummate that desire had created a physical block that prevented him from satiating it with anyone else.

Jake moved in his sleep, his dark eyebrows drawn together in a frown. A wave of love coursed through her as Stephanie watched him, melting her doubts. In the end, her choice was a simple one. Was her love for him deep enough to make her overcome her own dread and anguish, or was it too selfish to make that sacrifice?

He had told her that never again would he attempt to make love to her without invitation, but that didn't preclude *her* from making love to him.

Sliding off the robe she had been wearing, Stephanie approached the bed. If he woke up now, she thought, she might die of sheer embarrassment, because she was fairly certain that if he did he would send her back to her own room, rejecting her. His admission had not been made in any form of plea, but rather as a tortured, bitter gesture, meant to reinforce the gulf that now existed between them.

The night was relatively warm, and the quilt slid easily from his shoulders as she moved it gently away, taking care not to wake him.

The bed dipped as she kneeled down on it, and

she held her breath as Jake muttered something in his sleep and moved restlessly. He was lying on his stomach, and her muscles tensed as his restless movements caused the quilt to slide away completely, revealing the long line of his spine.

Her glance skidded and faltered over the angular tautness of his buttocks and then skimmed the length of his legs, tanned and darkened by a rough scattering of hair.

Closing her eyes, Stephanie drew a deep breath. She had already gone a long way from the girl who had felt only acute nausea at the mere thought of a man's body—the past few weeks had taught her that, but, even so, she had been wholly unprepared for her tangible physical response to Jake's nudity. She *wanted* to touch him, and a mixture of pain and delight flared to life inside her as she touched her lips gently to the smooth skin at the nape of his neck. Her hair spilled on to his shoulder and she smoothed the warm skin, exploring the shape of the underlying muscles, a sensitive feminine radar she had not known she possessed registering the faint relaxation in Jake's body and responding to it, letting her fingers drift down his spine on the beginning of a journey which, she hoped, for him, would lead to freedom, but which, she knew, for her, would only result in further enslavement.

'Jake.' She murmured his name as she traced the indentation of his waist, feathering her lips over the angle of his hip bone.

'Umm . . .' Although still asleep, he shifted slightly, turning on to his side and curling his arm round her waist, his eyes tightly closed.

'Jake.' Her fingertips stroked upward along the dark arrowing of hair, enjoying the silky feel of it, her nails gently caressing the flesh beneath. 'Jake, I want you to make love to me.' She bent her head, and delicately ran her tongue along the line already investigated by her fingers, biting gently at his skin, until she felt the sudden tensing of his muscles that told her he was awake.

'Stephanie ...?' He said it disbelievingly, lifting his head, and grasping a handful of her hair to twist her face away from his body.

'Stephanie, what the hell?'

'I want you to make love to me.' She said it with quiet dignity, holding his gaze.

Slowly his eyes slid over her; the pale perfection of her breasts, the nipples pink and erect; the curving shadow of her waist before it rounded out to her hips; the flatness of her stomach.

His eyes switched back to her face, cold and flat. 'I don't know what you think you're playing at Stephanie—at least, I hope I don't know.'

'I want you,' she interrupted quietly. 'You were right, I was being a coward. You said you wouldn't make love to me unless I came to you and begged you.'

'I said if you wanted me to make love to you, you'd have to beg me,' Jake corrected her flatly. 'I didn't make any promises about doing so.'

'Then I'll just have to make love to you, won't I?' Stephanie said softly.

'Look, Stephanie. I can guess what you're doing, but I don't ...'

'Want me?' she cut in bravely. 'I think you're

lying to me, Jake, but I'm prepared to give you the benefit of the doubt, and there's really only one way to find out which of us is right, isn't there?'

Without waiting for him to respond, she bent her head, placing her lips to the pulse thudding in his throat. She felt him swallow against ridged muscles and knew a tiny flare of triumph as his tension increased.

Not daring to look at him, Stephanie continued her delicate seduction, letting her lips and hands tell him all the things she couldn't find the words for. Beneath her palm, his heart beat evenly, until she brushed her tongue lightly across each male nipple, when it thudded in tense reaction. When she touched him again, circling and teasing the hard nub of flesh, his fingers curled round her hair, his whole body tense, his curt, 'Stephanie . . .' a warning she decided not to ignore.

'Don't you like it?' She made her voice sound lightly teasing, lifting her head against the pressure of his fingers to smile at him. The brief movement brought her breasts into contact with his chest, sending tingling spears of pleasure through her body.

'That's not the point . . .' His voice was terse, and for the first time since she had known him, he did not meet her eyes when he spoke to her. Hope and triumph flared together. Pride held him aloof from her; well, she could understand that, but, for the first time she began to hope that his desire and her love could overcome that pride. Her hand brushed his thigh and she felt his muscles lock in repudiation, but nothing could conceal the sudden surge of desire he tried to check, and Stephanie tugged herself gently free of his grasp to touch her lips lightly again to his chest. This time, she felt the hard flaring of desire her touch aroused, and, when his fingers curled into her hair, it was to hold her against him, not to push her away.

'I shouldn't be letting you do this,' he muttered rawly, 'but, God help me, I've wanted it for too long. What you're doing to me is the embodiment of every fantasy I've ever imagined about you.' He shuddered deeply as his admission gave her the courage to touch him more intimately, exploring the male shape of him and exulting in the fierce surge of desire he was powerless to control. His mouth found the curve of her shoulder, ravaging it with biting kisses that aroused and excited, his hand cupping her breast. A thick male sound of appreciation shattered the silence, giving Stephanie the courage to pull away from him, and trace the hard muscle structure of his thigh with fingers that trembled slightly.

'My God, don't do that,' Jake protested hoarsely.

'Why? Don't you like it?' Her voice was almost as thick as his, and, in response, Jake groaned, curling her hand into his own and then placing it against his heart.

'That's how much I like it,' he muttered, watching her with eyes that glittered silvery grey with molten heat. 'I like it in ways I can't begin to describe to you.' He sat up, burying his mouth in her throat, moving it against her skin, in a rough demanding caress. Her throat arching beneath the pressure of his mouth, Stephanie felt him cup her breasts with his hands, rubbing his thumbs over their sensitive tips.

A hungry, aching sensation spread hotly through her body, making her moan his name and arch herself up against him. His mouth left her throat and moved towards her breast, his hand sliding away to investigate the curve of her waist.

'Your skin's like silk velvet,' Jake groaned against her breast, 'I can't wait to feel all of it against me.' His tongue caressed her nipple and Stephanie cried out with pleasure, feeling the shudder of response that ripped through Jake. She had aroused him just as she had intended, and now the time had come to let him take control of them both. Her body was instantly responsive to the rhythms he set it, her fingers tightening into his hair as he tugged, almost feverishly, on her nipple, his hand sliding between her thighs to incite and then soothe a searing need that made her deaf to anything but the singing pleasure of his touch.

'You're sending me up in flames,' Jake told her, his voice slurred with the passion he no longer attemped to conceal. 'Dear God, Stephanie, you do things to me I'd forgotten it was possible to do.

'Jake.' Her body shuddered with pleasure against him. 'Jake, make love to me . . . Please . . .'

'Hush . . . soon . . . soon,' he promised, pulling her down against him and stroking his hand the length of her body. A surge of intense pleasure lifted her against him, her hands locking behind his neck as her mouth opened beneath his, admitting his penetration of its moist sweetness.

Beneath her, Stephanie felt the cool cotton of the sheet, and she realised that Jake was laying her gently back on the bed. As he slowly released her, her fingers curled protestingly into his thigh, 'Jake, don't leave me.' Her whole body ached for his possession with a feverish need she didn't try to conceal . . . 'Jake . . .'

'Shush . . . it's all right. I just don't want to hurt you. You taste of honey and strawberries,' he murmured, bending over her, letting his mouth drift across her skin. 'I could almost eat you.' His teeth nipped gently at the curve of her breast and she arched up in a mute plea, trembling with the force of her emotions.

'Stephanie . . .' Her name seemed to come from deep inside him, the sound spilling out from his throat, and then lost against her skin, as his hands slid to her hips and his mouth moved caressingly downwards, tasting every tremulous satin inch. Her nails raked against his shoulder, her gasps of pleasure filling the thick silence enveloping them, as his teeth nipped gently against her inner thigh and she cried out her need to touch and kiss him as intimately as he was doing to her.

'I want it all, Stephanie,' Jake told her hoarsely, his lips now against her mouth, 'everything . . .'

He broke off to groan in protest as she moved down his body to scatter wild kisses along his thighs, pulling her into his arms and silencing her protests as his mouth ground down on hers, his body shuddering with the force of his desire.

Stephanie melted mindlessly against him, aware of the hard warmth of his chest crushing her breasts; the heat of his thighs as they parted her own, her body lifting and arching, wanting his possession.

'Now, Jake, please now,' she demanded huskily, pressing her mouth to his skin with feverish urgency, and as though her words were what he had been waiting to hear, he surged against her.

His mouth on hers absorbed her brief cry of surprised pain just as his body carried her through it to an exploding crescendo of pleasure; a pinnacle almost too beautiful to endure, so perfect that it could not last, and had to be allowed to shatter into a downward glide back to normality.

'Jake . . .'

She wanted to ask him if he was free now, but her voice was slurred. Her eyes stung with silly tears and, as though he knew they were there, Jake bent his head, licking her face dry with the rough warmth of his tongue. 'Go to sleep.' His voice was thick with emotion. 'We'll talk in the morning.'

She pulled away from him, intending to reach for her robe and go back to her own room, but his arm tightened round her waist, his other hand pushing her face back into the curve of his body.

'Where do you think you're going?'

'Back to my room. You told me to go to sleep . . .'

'Tonight you're not sleeping anywhere but in my arms. I need to feel you there, Stephanie, just to reassure myself that it wasn't all a dream. Stay with me.'

As though she had ever wanted to leave! Dear God, how was she going to live without him? His lovemaking had been a revelation; a banquet of sensations that would always remain sharply clear in her mind and after which starvation was preferable to trying to sublimate the hunger for him with anyone else.

'Stephanie . . . time to wake up . . .'

Drowsily, she burrowed into her pillow away from the soft male voice tempting her to quit sleep.

'Stephanie.'

Firm hands touched her shoulder and then withdrew and she opened her eyes grudgingly. She had liked that brief touch but she would have liked more, and then, as Stephanie opened her eyes properly and saw Jake standing by the bed, already dressed in a thin cotton shirt and tight-fitting jeans, the last vestiges of sleep fled. She struggled to sit up, and then subsided beneath the quilt as she realised that she wasn't wearing anything. The flush of colour that this knowledge brought was soon superceded by a far more intense surge of embarrassment as memories of the previous night came flooding back.

'Jake . . .'

'I've brought you a cup of coffee,' he told her easily, apparently oblivious to her embarrassment. 'You've got half an hour before Brice arrives.'

'I'll get dressed . . . as soon as you've gone.' She hunted wildly for some signs of her clothes and then remembered that she was in Jake's room

'Gone?' His eyebrows rose, his eyes mocking her. Everthing about him this morning seemed to glow with an electric energy that, for some reason, she resented. He seemed more vitally alive than usual, amusement deepening the creases at the corners of his mouth as he watched her.

'Oh, so you're a grouch, first thing in the morning, are you? Well, I do believe I know a cure for that, but unfortunately, right now, we don't have time. Remind me to show it to you later.'

'Jake, about last night . . .' She couldn't put it off any longer. Not when she was lying naked in his bed, her body still sensitised by his lovemaking, her skin still flushed and bruised . . .

Jake moved, putting the mug of coffee on the bedside table next to her, his collar pulling away from his throat and Stephanie felt as though her whole body were burning with shamed embarrassment as she saw the faint tell-tale marks on his skin.

'Left your mark on me, well and truly, didn't you?' His teeth gleamed in amusement as he caught the direction of her transfixed stare. 'Stephanie,' he murmured in a different tone, 'we have to talk. I know you're not indifferent to me—last night proved that.' Stephanie forced herself to keep her gaze fixed rigidly on the third button of his shirt, willing herself not to give way to the humiliation she could feel rising inside her in an inescapable tide. Had he guessed that she loved him? She couldn't endure his pity.

Fingers clenching into her palms, she said in a

stilted voice, 'We can't talk now, Jake. Brice will be arriving. You said so yourself. What happened last night wa ... happened ... I don't want to talk about it ... I think perhaps we were both a little mad ... These things happen, and I don't suppose either of us would deny that there are deep emotional ties linking us ... Mainly because of ... of my being attacked. I've been selfish I know, never stopping to think of the effect it might have had on you. I ...'

'Enough.'

She practically jumped when Jake's hard, angry voice cut through her stilted sentences. He moved towards the bed, leaning towards her, supporting himself on rigid arms as he stared angrily down into her face, all his earlier humour gone. 'I don't pretend to know what you're trying to say to me, Stephanie ... You can theorise and analyse as much as you like, but that doesn't detract one single jot from the fact that, last night ...' he swore suddenly, his ears picking up the sound of a car before hers did.

'That sounds like Brice,' he told her, 'but don't think I'm letting it end here. We'll talk about it tonight.'

He left her before she could speak, and when she heard him talking to Brice outside, she hurried into her own room, showering and dressing almost haphazardly. She had been saved from further humiliation now by Brice's arrival, but the threat still hung over her. What did Jake intend to say to her tonight? That he realised how she felt? That he felt sorry for her? A small moan forced itself through her clamped throat. Last night, in her urgent impulse to free Jake from what she had perceived as the prison she had unwittingly put him in she had never stopped to consider that she might be betraying herself to him. She couldn't deceive Jake, he knew her too well. He was bound to ask himself why she had responded to him so eagerly, far too eagerly for someone who was simply trying to help a friend. And then what? Then she would be forced to endure his pity, and possibly that of Susy as well when the two of them eventually got together.

'Stephanie, are you ready yet?'

His query put an end to further heart-searching. Downstairs she found both men in the kitchen. Jake was busy making toast, and pushed a plate of it towards her as she walked in.

'Sorry about this,' he apologised to Brice, 'but I'm afraid we overslept a little this morning.'

The atmosphere in the small kitchen suddenly became tense with a hundred unspoken thoughts. Stephanie willed herself not to blush as Brice looked at her. If Jake had shouted from the top of the stairs that they were lovers, he could have hardly made it plainer, Stephanie thought bitterly. What on earth had got into him? He was normally so discreet and close-mouthed about his personal affairs. It was almost as though he wanted Brice to know what had happened between them. She pushed away her toast uneaten, suddenly feeling acutely sick.

'I'm not hungry,' she told him listlessly. 'I don't want to hold you up . . .'

'Where do you want to start?' Brice asked, diplomatically, glancing from Stephanie's pale face to Jake's hard one. 'I've arranged a meeting for you at twelve with the lawyers, and then there's lunch afterwards. I'm afraid you and I aren't included in that,' he apologised to Stephanie, 'only because we didn't realise you would be coming.'

'That's all right. It will give me an opportunity to do some sightseeing.' She was speaking for the sake of speaking, but jumped and was completely surprised when Brice said eagerly, 'Well, if that's the case, you must let me be your guide. No, I insist,' he continued when she opened her mouth to refuse. 'Miami isn't exactly the safest place in the world. I'm sure Jake wouldn't want you wandering around all by yourself.' His eyebrows rose as he looked at Jake for confirmation, but the grey eyes were hooded and cold.

'Stephanie must do whatever she wishes,' he said curtly. 'Personally, I would have thought there was enough to keep her entertained here without her having to go to Miami.'

In normal circumstances, Stephanie could have thought of nothing more enjoyable than spending the day exploring the site and the shore beyond it, but today, some perverse inclination made her say stubbornly, 'No, I'd be bored here. I'd rather go to Miami . . .'

If the truth were known she was afraid to stay behind because if she stayed she wouldn't be able to stop remembering last night . . . the heated urgency of Jake's lovemaking . . . the sounds of need and hunger he had stifled against her skin, and the pleasure he had taken in eliciting complementary sounds of need from her. Against

her will, she felt her body respond to those
memories, her breast swelling, her nipples taut
against the thin silk of her bra. As though he
knew exactly what was happening to her, Jake's
head turned, his eyes inspecting her slowly. All
the strength and breath seemed to drain out of
her, leaving her limp, and yet aching with a
curious emptiness.

'Are you sure you really want to go to Miami?
You don't look up to it to me.'

Stephanie hoped that Brice wouldn't interpret
the sexually loaded tone of Jake's voice as easily
as she could. Even the way Jake was looking at
her was a smouldering reminder of last night.
Her legs were boneless and she just about
managed to stop herself from turning to him.

'I'm fine,' she lied brittly, 'absolutely fine.'

'You know best,' Jake's tone suggested that she
knew nothing of the sort, but Stephanie ignored
it, following both men out to the car. This time,
Jake didn't sit in the back with her, for which she
was heartily grateful.

This time, she was more aware of the scenery
as they drove back along the route they had
travelled the previous evening. Jake had decided
that they would leave a full examination of the
site until the following day. As they arrived in
Miami with an hour to spare before his interview,
Brice took them both into his office, introducing
them to some of his staff. 'I've got some PR stuff
to show you, but we'll wait for that until the
contract's finally signed. What do you think of
the villas now that you've spent the night in one?'

'They're fine—as far as I can judge, but I'll

want an independent surveyor's report before the
contract's signed. That's something I've already
organised from the London end though, so you
don't need to concern yourself with that.'

'Well, I hope all goes well,' Brice smiled when
the three of them stood in the foyer of the
lawyer's building. 'Stephanie and I will see you
back here at about three, if that's okay?'

'Fine,' Jake sounded terse, but Stephanie
suspected it was because his mind was on the
coming interview. He probably didn't mean to be
curt with Brice, but that was how he came across,
and she felt slightly uncomfortable as she
accompanied Brice out into the late autumn
sunshine.

'Quite a man, your boss,' he commented,
smiling at her, 'but then, I guess you don't need
me to tell you that?'

With those few words, Stephanie knew that
Brice was aware of the relationship between Jake
and herself, and she bit her lip, not knowing what
to say.

'I meant it—about that job offer I mean,' he
said quietly, as he guided her towards his parked
car. 'If you should ever want a job, it's there.'

'What makes you think I might?' Her throat
was tight with pain and tears she dared not shed.

'Oh, something that tells me that you're not the
sort of girl to have an affair with her boss because
she thinks it might advance her career. Leaving
that aside, and in view of Jake's manner this
morning, I guess you must be in love with the
guy and . . .'

'And you also managed to deduce that he isn't

in love with me, otherwise he'd never have let you see that,' Stephanie struggled for the words, and then managed, 'that we spent the night together . . .'

'Hey now, hold on one second,' Brice protested, helping her into the car, and then manoeuvring it out into the busy, pre-lunchtime traffic. 'I never said that at all. All Jake did was let me know that you weren't available—a pretty natural reaction if you're involved with him. It was *your* expression that told me that you might be grateful for a hole to bolt into. I'm not going to pry,' he added, when he saw her white, tense face, 'all I am saying is that if you want a change of scene—for whatever reason, I'd like first refusal.'

'On what?'

'What?' Brice's eyes narrowed. 'On your services as a secretary,' he told her quietly. 'You see, I know how high Jake's standards are. If you're good enough for him, you must be first rate, and a first-rate secretary is something I could use.'

'What's the matter with whoever you've got working for you now?'

'Oh, she's fallen in love with me,' he told her casually, 'and being in love and efficiency just don't go together . . .'

At his side, Stephanie stiffened. Were all men callous and unfeeling? 'She's fallen in love with me,' he had said as though he were talking about nothing more important than the weather.

Brice must have registered her tension because he glanced at her and said disarmingly, 'Don't look like that. I guess I've put it badly. Perhaps I should have told you first, that *I've* fallen in love with *her*, and that my efficiency's gone to pot as well.' He grinned ruefully at her. 'We're getting married next month, and when we do, she says I've got to find another secretary.'

Stephanie managed to laugh, but it was a high, strained sound.

'Look, why don't I take you to meet her?' Brice suggested. 'I've given her the day off and she said she'd spend it in the house we've bought. I'd like her to meet you.'

'To give me her seal of approval as a potential substitute?' Stephanie asked drily. That seemed to be her role in life at the moment. Substituting for other and more dearly loved women.

'All right,' she conceded. It was a way of passing the time . . . of trying to tame her chaotic thoughts while she decided how she could avoid the "talk" Jake had said they were going to have, and which she would give anything to avoid.

CHAPTER TEN

STEPHANIE noticed the dark clouds massing on the horizon as they drove out of town, but thought nothing of it until Brice said worriedly, 'I hope that isn't the tail end of Hurricane Elaine we can see building up over there.'

'Hurricane Elaine?' Stephanie's alarm showed in her voice.

'Don't worry. It's not quite as bad as it sounds. By rights we're out of the hurricane season now, but Elaine's proving somewhat capricious. It said on the radio this morning that she wasn't going to hit Miami, but those clouds up ahead don't look too promising.'

His comment did nothing to calm Stephanie's fears. 'Do you think we ought to turn back?' she asked uncertainly. 'Jake . . .'

'I doubt we'll get more than a bad rainstorm,' Brice soothed. 'If you like, we'll ring for a weather check once we reach the house. It's not far now.'

The house Brice and his fiancée had bought was in a small township seventy miles from Miami. A pretty blonde-haired girl came running out on to the drive when Brice pulled up outside, and Stephanie felt a sharp stab of envy pierce her when she and Brice embraced.

'Honey, I think I've found your replacement,' Brice announced when he eventually released her.

Feeling awkward and embarrassed, Stephanie was conscious of being surveyed by a pair of warm, brown eyes.

'No way,' came the firm response, 'she's far, far too pretty, Brice.'

'She's also in love with someone else, isn't that so, Stephanie?' Brice asked her. 'Hollie, honey, Stephanie here works for Jake Lorrimer. You remember, the English guy . . .'

'Of course I do. Who could forget a man like Jake?' She rolled her eyes and smiled warmly at Stephanie. 'Come on in. I'll make us all a cup of coffee; not that you deserve one,' she teased Brice, 'driving beautiful women all over the estate whilst I'm slaving away here, trying to get this place cleaned up before we move in.'

Stephanie took to Hollie Brewster straight away, and found herself responding to her warm friendliness. It was Hollie who kicked Brice warningly under the table when he started to explain why Stephanie might want to change her job, giving Stephanie an understanding look as she did so.

'I don't like the look of those clouds,' she commented reinforcing Stephanie's earlier fears. 'They've been building up all day. Have you noticed how quiet it's gone outside?'

'I'll ring the weather centre. I meant to do it before.'

While he was gone, Hollie poured them all a fresh cup of coffee. 'I'm as thrilled as can be that we've found this house,' she confided in Stephanie. 'Brice owns an apartment in Miami, but it's not a place to bring up kids, and I aim to have at least two. Would you be seriously interested in working over here?'

'I don't honestly know,' Stephanie admitted. 'I just know that . . .' She broke off as Brice came back into the kitchen, frowningly worried. 'We'd better start back for Miami. The forecast isn't so good. We're due to catch the tail end of Elaine later on this afternoon. Nothing to worry about,' he hurriedly reassured Hollie. 'You'll be fine here, but heavy storms are forecast and the road between here and the main highway isn't too good.'

As he spoke, Stephanie glanced at her watch. 'We would have had to start back soon anyway. We've got to pick Jake up at three.'

Stephanie diplomatically headed for the car, leaving Brice and Hollie alone to say their goodbyes. Although she liked the American girl, meeting her had reinforced her own heartache, making her all too aware that Jake would never look at her the way Brice looked at Hollie.

As they drove away from the house thunder rumbled warningly in the distance, vivid flashes of lightning tearing apart the heavy grey clouds now lining the horizon. Inside the car, Brice turned off the air conditioning as the temperature suddenly dropped sharply, and started to whistle tunelessly between his teeth.

The storm clouds spread so quickly that one moment it was light and the next it was almost dark, only the rapid-fire lightning providing any illumination.

'I don't like this,' Brice muttered, hurriedly switching on his windscreen wipers as the rain started. Stephanie had never seen rain like it. It fell earthwards in straight sheets, so heavy that the windscreen wipers simply could not cope. The road they were travelling was a minor one whose maintenance was the responsibility of the township, and which had suffered some damage during the spring in similar storms. The area they were driving through was still partially swamp, and Stephanie remembered admiring the mango trees lining the road as they drove down it. Now she could only catch glimpses of them when the lightning forked. Brice had slowed down to a crawl because of the density of the rain, and later, Stephanie realised that this was probably what saved them from a fatal accident. She was just glancing at her watch, worrying about whether they would make it back to Miami in time to pick Jake up when she heard thunder rumble deafeningly overhead. Lightning followed, lighting up the road ahead, striking right into the heart of a huge tree.

Stephanie knew she must have cried out in shocked fear because she heard Brice's tense response. The car skidded on the wet road as he braked, and she closed her eyes only opening them when the abrupt cessation of movement jerked her head against the windscreen.

'Stephanie, are you okay?'

Brice sounded as shaken as she felt.

'Fine,' she assured him, touching trembling fingers to her forehead. No doubt, she would have a bruise there tomorrow, right now, all that mattered was that they were both alive and unhurt.

'We can't go on,' Brice told her. 'That falling tree's blocked the road and it's the only one out of town. We'll have to go back. I'll ring Jake from the house and explain what's happened. God, that was a near miss.' The shock was still in his voice, and Stephanie shivered in response to it, trying to make her tense body relax as he re-started the car and carefully reversed it over the wet road.

Stephanie had never been as relieved to see anything in her life as the lights of Brice's house when they eventually drew up outside it, unless it had been Jake that night two years ago when . . .

'Brice . . . Stephanie . . . my God, what's happened to you?' Hollie ushered them inside, exclaiming in concern as she saw how shocked they were.

'Take Stephanie upstairs and let her bathe her forehead,' Brice told her. 'I've got to ring Miami and get in touch with Jake.'

As he picked up the phone, Stephanie lingered in the living room, aching to hear Jake's voice and yet not daring to ask if she could speak to him.

'I'll be able to get him at the lawyers',' Brice explained as he punched a number into the receiver, 'this shouldn't take long. I'll tell him not to expect us until the morning.'

Stephanie heard him speaking to someone, and asking for Jake. Seconds passed, and then she heard Brice saying, 'Jake? Yeah, it's Brice. Look, I'm at my place and Stephanie's here with me. We're spending the night here, the road . . .' He broke off, holding the receiver away from him so that Stephanie could hear the fuzzy static. 'Damn it all to hell, the phone lines are down . . . Never mind,' he comforted her, 'at least Jake knows where you are and that you're safe.'

'My goodness, you're certainly going to have a bruise there,' Hollie exclaimed ten minutes later as she examined the already darkening skin round Stephanie's hairline. 'Thank God Brice wasn't driving any faster.'

Stephanie shuddered. 'I know . . . I keep seeing that tree falling and thinking that we could have been under it.'

'Well, you're both safe now. The worst of the storm's past, and the road should be cleared by morning. Brice is going to report that it's blocked, and when he comes back I'll make us all some supper. I'm afraid none of the bedrooms are exactly comfortable at the moment, but we can offer you a bed and a duvet. It's a pity we're such different heights,' she added, eyeing Stephanie's slender height with envious eyes. 'I can't see you getting into any of my clothes—all I keep here at the moment are working jeans and shirts.'

'My suit will dry out overnight,' Stephanie assured her, glancing and grimacing at her reflection in the bathroom mirror. Her soft silk suit had got soaked in the dash from the car to the house and was now looking creased and crumpled, but having come so close to suffering a major accident, she couldn't feel particularly concerned about the condition of her clothers.

Supper was a rather subdued meal. Brice had reported the fallen tree and confirmed that it would be moved by morning, and when she had helped with the supper dishes, Stephanie excused herself, wanting to leave Brice and Hollie alone.

As she showered in the bathroom of her bedroom, she examined her bruised forehead, wincing slightly. There were other bruises on her body, faint discolourations which she knew had not come from the accident and a low ache started up in the pit of her stomach. What was Jake doing right now? She mustn't think about him, she told herself, she must accept that he could no longer be part of her life. 'Tonight we'll talk' he had told her. She sighed. What was there left for them to talk about that would not cause him guilt and her pain?

Sliding into bed, she paused to check the time on her watch; Brice hadn't said what time they would leave in the morning, but no doubt Hollie would wake her.

'How are you feeling this morning? I feel as though I've gone ten rounds with the world champ,' Brice commented, flexing his neck. 'There isn't a muscle in my body that doesn't ache.'

'I feel the same way,' Stephanie admitted. 'I suppose stopping like that jolted us both more than we knew.'

'You're both lucky to get off as lightly as you did,' Hollie told them, adding 'My, but that's a fine bruise you've got Steph . . . a little lower and you'd have a lovely black eye.'

'The phone still isn't working, so I think I'll drive you straight to the villa,' Brice told

Stephanie. 'Even if Jake didn't make it back there yesterday, it's where your clothes are, and we can always ring Miami from there to find out where he is.'

They set off half an hour later, and Stephanie grimaced as she looked down at her crumpled silk suit. She had managed to shampoo and dry her hair, thanks to Hollie's offer of the loan of a hairdryer, but the other girl's skin was much darker than hers and so the only make-up she was wearing was her lipstick. The shock of the accident had left her looking washed out and listless, the livid bruise on her forehead all the more noticeable because of her pallor.

As they drove past the spot where the tree had fallen, a gang of men were just clearing away the final remains, and Stephanie shuddered, averting her eyes.

'There, but for the grace of God . . .' Brice murmured. 'Kinda makes you think, doesn't it?'

'Umm . . .' Stephanie glanced at her wrist to check the time and realised that she had left her watch behind.

'Don't worry about it. I'll get it back to you,' Brice promised. He turned on the radio so that they could listen to the news and Stephanie was relieved to hear that the hurricane had changed course during the night and had missed Miami completely.

'Happens that way with hurricanes. Unpredictable things—that's why they're always given female names,' Brice grinned.

By the time they drew up outside the villa, Stephanie was tense with nervous dread. She wanted to see Jake and yet she didn't, and then Brice murmured, 'Well, Jake's hire car's here, and it's been moved, so it looks as though he got back last night.' He glanced at his watch and frowned. 'Look, I'd better not come in with you. By rights, I ought to be in my office right now. Tell Jake I'll ring him later on, will you, and remember Steph, that job offer's open if you want it.'

As Stephanie let herself into the villa, Brice was reversing his car. She heard him drive away as she stepped into the living area, almost too weary to put one foot in front of the other. Her head was pounding with pain, and all she wanted to do was to lie down.

'Some night that must have been if he didn't even want to see you safely inside.'

'Jake!' Stephanie tensed, as he pushed open the kitchen door, unable to drag her eyes away from the dark fury of his face.

'Why did you do it, Stephanie?' he demanded savagely, coming towards her. 'To make sure he offered you that job? Was it as good with him as it was with me? *Was* it?' he grated, reaching out and curling his fingers into her hair, pulling her round until her face was in the light.

'My God . . .' His fingers touched her bruised face, the look in his eyes so ragingly contemptuous that she had to close her own against it. 'Is that what you like?' His voice came from somewhere above her, almost rusty with an emotion she could only interpret as anger. 'All this time, I've been treating you with velvet gloves, and yet you went to him and let him . . .'

'Jake, please . . .' She was almost too exhausted to explain to him.

'Please what? Open your eyes, Stephanie. I want to see what you're really feeling when you say, "please" to me. Please what ? Let you go so that you can go to him; is that it? You liked what he did to you last night so much you want more?'

'Jake, you don't understand.' She couldn't understand what had got into him; why he should be making such unfounded accusations.

'Oh, I understand all right,' he told her with soft savagery. 'I understand that you went from my bed straight to his, and that, by the looks of you, he threw you out of it much the same way that he threw you out of his car. Is *that* what happened when you were attacked, Stephanie? Did it make it impossible for you to respond to any man who didn't treat you violently?'

'Jake . . .' Her voice was a broken whisper of protest. 'That's . . . that's a horrible thing to say . . .'

'Is it ? When I made love to you, you responded to me so passionately that I thought . . .'

Dangerbells rang warningly in Stephanie's mind. Panic stricken by the thought that Jake might be going to say he knew she loved him, she interrupted swiftly, 'You thought what? That making love to me gave you exclusive rights to me? All right,' she rushed on recklessly. 'All right, so I slept with Brice. Why shouldn't I? You don't own me, Jake. I'm a free agent. I can . . .'

She broke off as she heard someone knocking

on the door. Jake thrust her away from him and, as he did so, she noticed that beneath his tan his face seemed to have aged, the lines running from nose to mouth deepening as though he had sustained great pain.

'Perhaps it's your latest lover, come to make amends,' Jake taunted throwing open the door.

To Stephanie's surprise, it was Hollie who stood there, her smile fading as she looked from Stephanie's pale face to Jake's hard one.

'Hi,' she said uncertainly. 'Looks like I came at a bad moment, but I've brought your watch back Steph. You left it last night and since I had to go shopping, I thought I might as well drop it off on the way. I won't stop,' she added. 'I'm having lunch with Brice so that we can get the final arrangements for the wedding sorted out.' She handed Stephanie her watch.

'The wedding?' Without taking his eyes off Stephanie, Jake asked the soft question.

'Yeah, didn't Brice tell you?' Hollie queried, whilst Stephanie willed her not to say any more. 'It's only a month away now, and we're working like beavers to get the house we've bought ready.'

'The house?'

'Yeah . . . In Charlotteville. I guess Stephanie hasn't had a chance to tell you about it yet. I suppose you're cussing Brice for bringing her out to see me yesterday, but for that she'd have been safe from the storm in Miami. Look, I'll have to go . . . but maybe we'll all be able to get together before you leave?'

'So last night you slept with Brice,' Jake said softly when Hollie had gone. 'Now, tell me, what was Hollie doing whilst you were making love to her fiancé?'

Feeling trapped, Stephanie could only stare at him. How on earth could she manage to explain? As her eyes met Jake's, she knew there was only one way.

'Jake, I didn't sleep with Brice, but you seemed so determined to believe that I had that it was easier to . . .'

'Lie?' he offered, watching her.

'All right, I did lie. I lied because . . .'

'Because?' Jake prompted softly. It was too much for Stephanie. His soft questions were driving her into a trap, as though he already knew what she was trying to hide from him.

'Because I didn't want you to feel sorry for me.' She took a deep breath and lifted her head, meeting his gaze proudly. 'To feel that you owed me anything. To think . . .'

'That because you'd crawled into my bed and made love to me that it meant you actually loved me. Is that what you're trying to tell me?'

'Yes.'

A nerve jumped in his jaw.

'Meaning that it was just a one-off thing, that you don't want to repeat?'

'Yes.'

'Ah well, as you said to me the other night, there's only one way to find out if you're telling the truth.'

'Jake, put me down!' She gasped out the protest as he moved, too quickly for her to avoid him, picking her up as easily as though she were a child, carrying her determinedly towards and up the stairs.

In his room, the covers were thrown back from the bed, the pillow still bearing the imprint of his head. He dropped her on to the bed and then followed her there, trapping her struggling body with the superior weight of his.

'Stop fighting me,' he ordered. 'If you're telling the truth you've got nothing to fear, have you? I know enough about women to know when one's responding to me or not, Stephanie.' His fingers curled round the top of her silk suit, unfastening the small pearl buttons.

'When you told me you had slept with Brice, was it because you wanted to punish me?'

'Jake, please.' Stephanie ignored his question, trying to push his hands away from her skin. He had peeled back her top completely and was slowly tracing a line along the lacy barrier of her bra, too intent on his journey even to lift his eyes to hers.

'Answer me, Stephanie . . .'

'Jake, if you don't stop this, you'll make me hate you,' she protested wildly.

'You'll *hate* me?' Now his eyes did lift, a dispassionate interest in their depths as they searched her pale face. 'You'll hate this?' His hand freed her breasts from her bra and caressed their pale softness, 'and this . . .' When he bent his head and touched his mouth to their rosy crests, she breathed in sharply, willing her body against response, but it was useless. She was shaking like a leaf, torn between self-contempt and molten desire. Jake's hands moved deftly over her body, removing her remaining clothes while she protested feverishly against the intimacy, her fingers clutching at the lapels of his shirt.

'Jake, I don't want you to do this.' She moaned the protest deep in her throat, fighting against the fires he had ignited inside her.

'You don't? Touch me, Stephanie.' he murmured. 'Take my shirt off and touch me as you know you want to.'

'No . . .'

But it was no use. Jake's mouth was exploring the sensitive skin of her throat, his hands caressing her body, and she couldn't stop herself from sliding her palms into his shirt, from breathing in the male scent of him. Without warning, Jake's mouth suddenly captured her own, forcing her head back and her lips to part for the deep, thrusting invasion of his tongue. Fire licked through her veins, burning away all restraint, consuming her in a heat that craved more of his touch.

'So you don't want me?' Jake murmured, as he released her swollen mouth, stroking it with his tongue, biting gently at the soft contours, 'and you don't want this?' He cupped her breast, the weight of his lower body crushing her back against the mattress as he bent his head, his mouth against her breast, caressing the swelling nipple, the sensually rhythmic movements of his body against hers increasing the sharp hunger rising moltenly through her body, until she was responding mindlessly to it.

She wanted him so badly. She loved him so much. She trembled as Jake raised his head, knowing that he was looking at her. As he watched her, his thumb stroked caressingly over her nipple, his hand leaving her breast to run slowly along her silky skin to her thigh. The delicate patterns his fingers inscribed against her skin were a subtle form of torture designed purely to make her aware of her own weakness. Against her will, her body arched, clamouring for the heat of his. The rough fabric of his jeans scraped her skin, but Stephanie didn't heed it. She needed and loved him with an intensity that overrode pride and caution. Her hands tugged away his shirt, her mouth finding the hard warmth of his shoulder and tasting the familiarity of it, and while she kissed him, worshipping him with feverish wild kisses, Jake did nothing. Her hands slid down his body, her fingers curling impatiently into his belt and then tensing.

'Go on,' Jake drawled, 'for a woman who doesn't want me, you have a very interesting way of showing it.'

His words were like ice, dripping down her spine, crushing her with their contempt. She pulled away, but Jake stopped her. 'Oh no,' he whispered softly. 'Is this what you want, Stephanie?'

She moaned softly, hating the searing bitterness in his voice as he held her to the bed and stripped off his jeans, her face turned away so that she would not have to look at him but she couldn't blot out all the tiny purposeful sounds, and even though she protested huskily when he came back to her, her body couldn't deny itself the contact it had craved. She wanted to feel his skin against hers, his hardness against her softness, his . . .

His hips moved seductively against her, eliciting a soft cry of pleasure. She felt Jake breathe deeply and then his arms were round her, binding her to his body, his mouth on hers in an urgent demanding kiss that she responded to blindly, almost reeling under its hard pressure.

When he released her, she felt as though she were suddenly surfacing from a long, deep dive, awareness of reality slowly returning, until she became conscious that he was depriving her body of the contact it craved with his, and she cried his name almost without being aware of it, reaching up for him. 'Jake, please . . .'

'Please, what?'

He looked down at her, his eyes narrowed and glittering, and Stephanie knew that it was too late to deny him, and that it had always been too late.

She closed her eyes on the tears she knew were there and said defeatedly, 'Please make love to me . . . please . . . please love me, even if it's only this once . . . even if it's all make-believe.'

'So, you *do* want me?' His eyes were unfathomable, shutting his thoughts away from her.

'You know I do.' The quiet admission was acutely painful to make.

'I wanted *you* for two years,' he reminded her softly. 'That's how long I had to wait for you, Stephanie. Two years is a long time for a man to go hungry for a woman.'

'Is that why you're doing this to me now? To punish me? I didn't *know* you wanted me, Jake.'

'Why did you come to me the other night?'

'I wanted to set you free.'

'To go to another woman?' He bent his head and feathered light kisses along her throat and her body responded mindlessly to the shivering pleasure of his touch.

'Is that what you want, Stephanie?' he pressed. 'For me to he go another woman?'

'No.' The admission seemed to have been wrung from her soul. Tears spilled helplessly down her face, her body aching with a pain of a different kind. 'No,' she admitted huskily, 'I want you to stay with me, to love me as . . .'

'As?'

'As I love you,' she admitted painfully, suddenly aware of the tension in Jake's body, the strain deepening the lines around his eyes.

'Stephanie! My God, at last!' His voice trembled unevenly over her name, his forehead damp as it rested against hers, and the tension drained out of his body. 'You can't know how much I've needed to hear you say that; how I've almost willed you into saying it at times. I love you.'

'You love me?' She couldn't believe it!

'Yes.'

When she would have spoken, he shook his head and said softly, 'I fell in love with you the day you walked into my office for the interview, although I didn't know it at the time. Then, I thought it was just desire. By the time you left I was visualising you not in my office but in my bed, and you seemed to be equally aware of me. Then, that night you were attacked. I can't begin to describe what I felt; and as the months went by and it became more and more obvious that, physically, you just couldn't be reached, I told myself my feelings for you would die, but they didn't. I dated other women——'

'Susy ...' Stephanie substituted, her fingers playing with the dark hair curling against his chest.

'Amongst others,' Jake agreed dryly. 'I even tried to make love to them, but ... That was when I knew how much I loved you. I couldn't believe it when I looked up at you one day and caught you watching me ... seeing me as a man, and not just as a friend. That was when I began to hope.'

'You were so angry with me, and I was so confused.'

'When a man's as frustrated as I was, he is apt to become "angry". The way you reacted to Susy was the most heartening thing of all, but I couldn't get you to admit how you felt, and then you started dating someone else. I can't begin to describe how I felt that evening when I drove round to see you and found you in his arms. I wanted to kill the pair of you.'

'I had no idea you loved me, and I was terrified when I realised how I felt about you.'

'But you still came to me and made love to me so sweetly that my guts still ache at the memory of it. When I thought you'd gone from me to Brice, I was like a man out of his mind. When he phoned to say you were spending the night with him ...' Stephanie felt the shudder that went through him and smiled tremulously. 'The phone line went dead before he could explain the situation ... I never dreamed you'd be jealous ...

I was so busy worrying about stopping you from discovering how I felt. I thought you might feel a responsibility towards me . . . that you might pity me.'

'Pity you?' His eyebrows arched. 'The only person I can find pity for right now is me. Starting now, you owe me two years of loving, and I fully intend to charge interest on the debt. You can make a start by promising to marry me the moment we get back to London, and then I think we'll take a long, long honeymoon so that you can start making interest payments on the capital.' When she didn't respond, he tensed and said roughly, 'Stephanie, you will marry me, won't you? Dear Heaven,' he groaned, 'I don't think I could stand it if you won't.'

'Oh, Jake, there's nothing I want more than to be your wife.' She caught her breath as he moved against her and admitted huskily, 'Well, almost nothing. It wasn't very fair of you to force me to admit how I feel.'

His warm laughter brushed her skin. 'Oh, Stephanie. If you weren't such a blind idiot, you'd have guessed months ago that I love you. Every time my body touches yours it's an admission of love. Let me show you,' he whispered against her ear. 'Let me show you, in all the ways there are, just what you mean to me. I love you so much.' His voice was raw with emotion, his arms tightening round her as he silenced her small murmur of pleasure with his mouth.

'You asked me to love you,' he murmured, moments later. 'I do, and I will.' His fingers

touched her bruised forehead, his expression
tense as he remembered the accusations he had
thrown at her. Reading his mind, Stephanie
caught his hand in hers, pressing her lips to his
palm. 'It doesn't matter,' she told him softly,
releasing his hand to open her arms to him, her
rescuer, her friend, her lover.

'All that matters is that we've found each other.
Even now, I can't believe I'm not dreaming.'

She felt Jake smile. 'Then let me prove it to
you,' he murmured, softly taking her in his arms.
'Love me, Stephanie,' he begged against her skin.
'Love me as much as I love you.'

'I do,' she assured him softly.

'Then show me.'

'We came here to work—remember?' Stephanie
teased him long moments later.

'So we did,' Jake agreed, 'but this is far, far
more important and certainly far more enjoyable,
don't you agree?'

She did, and she proved it to him by reaching
out to pull him down against her body, knowing
that this time she could show him without
restraint that her love was as deeply intense as
his.

ROMANCE

Next month's romances from Mills & Boon

Each month, you can choose from a world of variety in romance with Mills & Boon. These are the new titles to look out for next month.

SAVE MY SOUL FROM SIN Lindsay Armstrong
WRECKER'S BRIDE Kathryn Cranmer
RING OF CRYSTAL Jane Donnelly
OUT OF WEDLOCK Sandra Field
NEVER KISS A STRANGER Mary Gabriel
THE HABIT OF LOVING Rosemary Hammond
BLUEBEARD'S BRIDE Sarah Holland
THE FLAME TREE Elizabeth Graham
THE PASSIONATE LOVER Carole Mortimer
DRAGON MAN Elizabeth Oldfield
NO TIME FOR MARRIAGE Roberta Leigh
THE ROAD Emma Goldrick

Buy them from your usual paperback stockist, or write to: Mills & Boon Reader Service, P.O. Box 236, Thornton Rd, Croydon, Surrey CR9 3RU, England. Readers in South Africa-write to: Mills & Boon Reader Service of Southern Africa, Private Bag X3010, Randburg, 2125.

Mills & Boon
the rose of romance

Take 4 Exciting Books Absolutely FREE

Love, romance, intrigue... all are captured for you by Mills & Boon's top-selling authors. By becoming a regular reader of Mills & Boon's Romances you can enjoy 6 superb new titles every month plus a whole range of special benefits: your very own personal membership card, a free monthly newsletter packed with recipes, competitions, exclusive book offers and a monthly guide to the stars, plus extra bargain offers and big cash savings.

**AND an Introductory FREE GIFT for YOU.
Turn over the page for details.**

As a special introduction we will send you four exciting Mills & Boon Romances Free and without obligation when you complete and return this coupon.

At the same time we will reserve a subscription to Mills & Boon Reader Service for you. Every month, you will receive 6 of the very latest novels by leading Romantic Fiction authors, delivered direct to your door. You don't pay extra for delivery — postage and packing is always completely Free. There is no obligation or commitment — you can cancel your subscription at any time.

You have nothing to lose and a whole world of romance to gain.

Just fill in and post the coupon today to **MILLS & BOON READER SERVICE, FREEPOST, P.O. BOX 236, CROYDON, SURREY CR9 9EL.**

Please Note:- READERS IN SOUTH AFRICA write to Mills & Boon, Postbag X3010, Randburg 2125, S. Africa.

FREE BOOKS CERTIFICATE

To: Mills & Boon Reader Service, FREEPOST, P.O. Box 236, Croydon, Surrey CR9 9EL.

Please send me, free and without obligation, four Mills & Boon Romances, and reserve a Reader Service Subscription for me. If I decide to subscribe I shall, from the beginning of the month following my free parcel of books, receive six new books each month for £6.60, post and packing free. If I decide not to subscribe, I shall write to you within 10 days. The free books are mine to keep in any case. I understand that I may cancel my subscription at any time simply by writing to you. I am over 18 years of age.

Please write in BLOCK CAPITALS.

Signature _____

Name _____

Address _____

_____ Post code _____

SEND NO MONEY — TAKE NO RISKS.

Please don't forget to include your Postcode.

Remember, postcodes speed delivery. Offer applies in UK only and is not valid to present subscribers. Mills & Boon reserve the right to exercise discretion in granting membership. If price changes are necessary you will be notified.

6R *Offer expires June 30th 1985*

EP86